Medicine through the ages

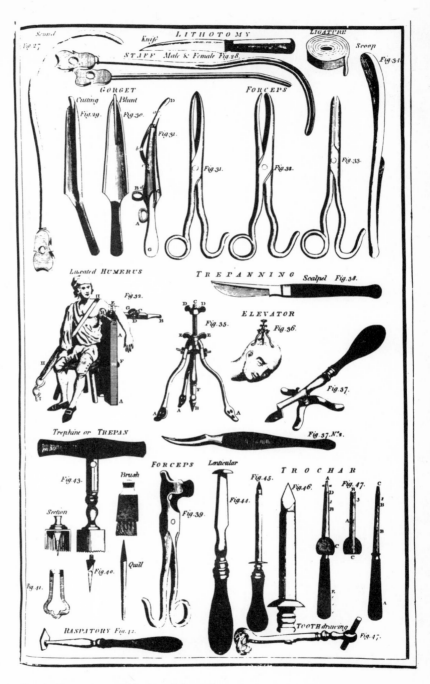

Surgical instruments of the late eighteenth century

Medicine through the ages

G. R. Davidson,
FRCS(Ed), FRACS

LONDON: Methuen & Co Ltd

NEW YORK: Roy Publishers Inc

First published 1968
by Methuen & Co Ltd
11 New Fetter Lane London EC4
and Roy Publishers Inc, New York 10021
© 1968 by G. R. Davidson
Phototypeset and printed in Great Britain
by BAS Printers Ltd
Wallop, Hampshire
Library of Congress Catalog No 68-12412

Preface

Although it could be argued that everyone plays a part in making history, for all practical purposes history is secondhand, and the author of even the shortest of medical histories is deeply indebted to many writers and observers.

This author has leant heavily on three eminent medical historians, Garrison, Guthrie and Singer, and material has been drawn from many different writers. Most of these sources have been mentioned in footnotes, but if any have been missed inadvertently, apologies and thanks are tendered.

An attempt has been made to tell in a consecutive way the story of medicine from the days of prehistory to the present time. It is to be expected that knowledgeable readers will be perturbed by what they consider and what almost certainly are obvious and regrettable omissions. When dealing with a wealth of material that is unmanageable in its abundance, it is obviously impossible to confine it within the small compass of a book such as this.

Lytton Strachey, in the preface of his book *Eminent Victorians*, writes : 'For ignorance is the first requisite of the historian — ignorance which simplifies and clarifies, which selects and omits with a placid perfection unattainable by the highest art.' The author apologises for his ignorance and omissions, but not for his selections, and certainly not for his subject.

His thanks are due to Methuen & Co, especially to Mr Julian Hodgson for help given in so many ways concerned with the writing and publication of this book.

Contents

Acknowledgments

Permission to reproduce photographs is
gratefully acknowledged to the Royal
College of Surgeons for the frontispiece and
those on pages 16, 18, 19, 24, 38, 45, 47, 48,
49, 57, 58, 59, 61, 64, 67, 78 and 79 ; to the
Wellcome Trust for those on pages 11, 27,
29, 55, 56, 73 and 79 ; to the British Museum
for that on page 15 ; to the Courtauld
Institute of Art for those on pages 46 and 68 ;
to the Mayo Clinic for those on page 70 ; to
the Royal Flying Doctor Service for that on
page 85 ; and to the Board of Governors,
Hammersmith Hospital, and the Royal
Postgraduate Medical School for that on
page 90.

1 The mysteries of prehistoric medicine

The beginnings of medicine are hidden in the mists of prehistory. No written records exist, of course, and even approximate dates must be regarded as being based on speculation and rough estimates. In the process of evolution, as his brain enlarged, man developed the capacity for constructive thought. This has enabled man, unlike all other forms of life, slowly and painfully to develop something we call culture. In its widest application this includes everything from religion to science and medicine as well as the more obvious forms of artistic expression. Almost certainly, in the course of man's development, something like the following must have occurred.

In a cave, lit occasionally by the flames from a smoky fire, the figure of a woman can be seen. Crouching in a corner near the fire she clutches to herself the feverish body of her first child, and in fear and misery she rocks slowly backwards and forwards. Suddenly she comes to a decision. Calling her mate, she shows him once again the hot moaning child and points to the swollen redness under the left arm. Protests die on his lips and seizing his spear he creeps out of the cave into the terrors and dangers of a prehistoric night.

To the waiting woman an age seems to pass before he returns, accompanied by another member of the cave-dwelling community. There is nothing to distinguish the newcomer, except perhaps the small skin bag that is attached to a thong around his waist and the feeling of confidence he seems to have brought into the cave with him. After he has examined the child, events follow quickly. The flint knife is taken from the bag ; the quick stabbing cut and the feeble cry are followed by the flow of pus and eventually quiet sleep.

On that night, in that cave, history was made if not recorded. Although quite unaware of it, man had, as the smoke wreathed upwards, taken the first step of that unending climb that leads to the stars. Perhaps a spark from that fire ignited the flame that has burnt, sometimes fitfully, sometimes fiercely, through the ages since that time.

The story of medicine briefly records how that flame has been kept alight. Admittedly this has been done before, many times, but it cannot be done too often because in the practice of medicine, at its best, man fulfils his highest destiny.

It is perhaps not purely coincidental that the three subjects which throughout history have caused most commotion, lack of agreement and general mayhem should be religion, politics and medicine. The link

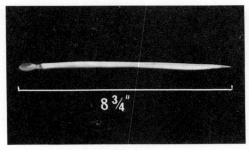

1 *Aboriginal pointing bone*

between these three subjects goes back a very long way, but becomes quite obvious when it is remembered that witch-doctors or medicine-men constituted the earliest professional class in the evolution of society.

Nearly always they occupied a unique and powerful position. Frequently the witch-doctor was the agent who translated into action the policy (or politics) of his particular tribe. His power was not surprising when certain beliefs held by primitive people of today and certainly by their prehistoric counterparts are considered. They felt that man was at first designed to be immortal, and legends and folklore exist in many different parts which illustrate the widespread belief that death, and the disease that so often preceded it, came to mankind as a punishment for disobedience or sin.

The description of the eating of the forbidden fruit in the Garden of Eden is the Biblical version of such a legend. Disease resulting from natural causes was not recognised. Almost inevitably such misfortunes were regarded as being due to the malevolent activities of some enemy either supernatural or human. Such activities could take the form of the introduction of some harmful substance or influence (such as an evil spirit) into the body of the victim,

10

or the abstraction of the mind or soul. The age-old custom of pointing the bone, which is still practised by the Australian aborigines, is an example of both these methods. Here is a description of the act taken from Idriess's book *Lasseter's Last Ride*.[1]

'The witch-doctor, crooning and swaying on his squatting haunches, held a long sharp pointed bone in the direction of the victim. Three other men, squatting at intervals behind him, held clear of the ground a twelve-foot-long cord of human hair attached to the bone. The last man held a bone cylinder in which the end of the cord was fastened. They were pointing the bone, 'singing' someone to death. The words of the insinuating croon, speeded in the direction pointed by the bone by diabolical agency, were supposed to have the power of taking a little blood from the victim and drawing it invisibly through space into the bone, sucking it along the cord into the bone receptacle. The witch-doctor, thus having possession of the victim's life-blood, could poison him through it with disease.'

Any Australian aboriginal at whom the bone is pointed will surely die.

Because of the widely held belief that

[1] Idriess, Ion L., *Lasseter's Last Ride,* 16th ed., p 200. Angus and Robertson Ltd (1934).

2 *Trepanned skull*

many diseases were the result of possession by an evil spirit or devil, what could be more logical than the assumption that the best way to get rid of the unwelcome visitor was to make its habitation so supremely uncomfortable that it would not want to stay ? On some occasions an easy way of escape for the evil spirit was also provided. Examples of the first methods practised by witch-doctors or priest-physicians ranged from incantations, dances, strong drugs and painful bandages to actual physical violence which included flogging and imprisonment.

Examination of the skulls of prehistoric men, unearthed in many different parts of the world, has shown evidence of the strange surgical operation of trephining or trepanning. In this operation a circular portion of the skull was removed, probably by scraping through the bone with a sharp flint. It is known that this operation is practised by some primitive races of today. Sometimes it has been carried out in the course of treatment of a skull fracture or perhaps for the relief of severe headache, epilepsy, insanity or blindness. More often than not, no evidence of any skull fracture is found and the generally accepted explanation of this strange procedure, whether practised by primitive, modern or prehistoric peoples, is that an opening was

provided to give an evil spirit or demon an easy avenue of escape.

Such an operation, even when carried out with all the resources of modern surgery and anaesthesia, is never regarded as a minor procedure. Therefore it is all the more amazing to find that when these particular primitive skulls are examined, the edges of many of the trephined openings are rounded and smooth, showing definite evidence of healing. As such changes in bone occur only slowly, this indicates that the patient had survived the operation and had lived for a considerable time afterwards.

The first of these skulls to be brought to public notice was unearthed by a French physician and archaeologist in 1865. It is interesting to think about this date, because in the same year another very important event occurred. In March of that year, Lister first used his antiseptic methods in the successful treatment of a compound fracture of the leg. In pre-Listerian days a surgical opening of the skull usually ended fatally with infection and terminal meningitis (inflammation of the membranes lining the brain). It is interesting to speculate what might have occurred if the skulls had been excavated a hundred years earlier. Would anyone have said, 'Why did so many of these cases live and why do so many of ours die ? Could it be that a flat rock in the sun is better than a grimy hospital operating room, and a flint scraper (which soon wears and is discarded) is safer than a sharp (but dirty) metal knife ?' If the questions had been asked, could they have been answered ? Probably not : the world has always had to wait for its Listers.

However, there is no doubt that the influence of this theory of 'possession by evil spirits or demons' lasted a very long time. It was responsible for the association between medicine and religion and for the develop-ment of the witch-doctor and later the priest-physician. Not until the days of Hippocrates, the true father of medicine, were these beliefs seriously questioned. From that time medicine gradually became divorced from magic and religion. However, old beliefs die hard and the theory of possession by devils has undoubtedly influenced our thought from the earliest days of prehistory.

There seems little doubt that these ideas existed fairly generally up to the end of the eighteenth century and quite probably, in some ways, even affect us today. As J. M. Calder observed in her book, *The Story of Nursing*,[1] 'There is no doubt that through its influence the life of the leper was made more miserable and the mentally sick were treated with incredible cruelty.'

The study of the mind is still in its infancy. Who can say that some of the fears and worries of today, such as fear of darkness and fear of being alone, are not legacies from some far distant past ? Even amongst people with a long history of civilisation, medicine and magic are still confused. The wearing of charms and amulets is common practice and examples of folk medicine are found in many forms all over the world.

It seems reasonable to assume that, coincidentally with the evolution of the witch-doctor caste, other individuals developed who also interested themselves in healing, but in a simpler and less spectacular form. Such people treated minor maladies, often by using plants and other simple remedies. From their unrecorded efforts, herbalism started, and many of the beginnings of the modern folklore of today

[1] Calder, J. M., *The Story of Nursing*, p 11. Methuen's Outlines, 4th ed. (1963).

12

came from such people as well as from the witch-doctor hierarchy.

History is the bridge which connects the past through the everchanging present with the future. If we make intelligent use of this bridge we may understand a little more clearly why we react to certain situations the way we do and we may understand a little better certain of our worries. For example we can now appreciate, perhaps only partly, why the waters of Abana and Pharphar[1] are still popular spas, and the road to Endor[2] a well-known thoroughfare for those seeking medical help. We might even have a slight clue as to why certain people, somewhat irreverently perhaps, refer to present day psychiatrists as 'head-shrinkers'.

[1] 2 Kings V, 12.
[2] 1 Samuel XXVIII, 7–25.

2 The dawn of civilisation

After this long prehistoric period we come to the dawn of recorded history, made possible by the invention of writing and the development of the calendar. The alphabet as we know it represents the last stage in the long history of writing. Probably the first developments took place in the great Sumerian civilisation which evolved in the fertile valleys between the Euphrates and Tigris rivers in Mesopotamia about 4000 B.C. The ancient city known later as Ur of the Chaldees was the capital of this Empire. A considerable part of this city has been excavated, revealing the greatness of the Sumerian culture. This culture may have preceded and at least equalled, if it did not surpass, the better-known Egyptian civilisation.

There can be no doubt that a Sumerian medical profession existed. Evidence suggesting this is found on certain clay tablets that have been excavated, and there is, in the Wellcome Historical Medical Museum in London, a seal of a Sumerian physician who practised about 3000 B.C. The Sumerian civilisation came to an end when the country was invaded and divided by the Babylonians and the Assyrians about 2000 B.C.

One of the early Babylonian kings, by the name of Hammurabi, drew up a famous Code of Laws which was engraved on stone and set up in the temple in Babylon. From this code we learn that the medical profession was entitled to charge certain fees which were prescribed and regulated by law. Severe penalties were imposed for unsuccessful surgery. These were often very drastic and included the loss of both hands. It seems amazing, under these circumstances, that any form of surgery was carried out at all. However, despite these hazards there is evidence that a well organised medical profession existed in those times. Although magic and divination entered greatly into medical treatment, an outstanding achievement in hygiene took place when the infective nature of leprosy was recognised and lepers, in consequence, were expelled from the community.

Egyptian medicine

It is known that in Egypt as early as 4000 B.C. a society with an organised government existed. It is also known that methods of recording time and events were in use, just as they were in the coexisting Sumerian civilisation.

The main sources of our knowledge of Egyptian medicine come not only from engravings on clay tablets, door-posts of tombs and the like, but also from certain

3 *Bronze statuette of Imhotep*

medical papyri, the oldest of which dates back to perhaps 2160 B.C. To Egypt goes the honour of having the earliest recorded physicians, and we find that there are two rival claimants for the unique position of the first physician in history. They are Sekhet'enanach and Imhotep. As the first-mentioned lived about twenty years earlier than his rival, perhaps the title should be given to him. However Imhotep, who lived about 2980 B.C., is much better known to medical historians. For years after his death he was worshipped as a demigod at Memphis and temples were dedicated to his honour. As well as being a physician he was also a successful statesman and a very great architect. He was responsible for the erection of the oldest surviving stone building in the world, the Step Pyramid of Sakharah.

Bronze statuettes of this remarkable man exist and some may be seen in the British Museum and in the Wellcome Historical Medical Museum. In Imhotep's temple at Memphis and in other temples dedicated to him, although facilities existed for the worship of the gods, other parts of these buildings served as a type of hospital where the sick were treated and young physicians were trained. Along with these developments medicine gradually became regarded as being of divine origin ; the cult of the priest-physician became the bond between religion and medicine, and magic became less important.

The Egyptian physicians were versed in the use of elaborate prescriptions, and one of the most important of the medical papyri (The Ebers Papyrus) contains descriptions of more than 700 prescriptions and remedies. Through the ages the really great physicians have endeavoured to simplify medicine and the drugs and remedies that they used. This Egyptian multiplicity of prescriptions might be regarded, on first thought, as being an example of advancement. In reality, however, it represented a form of decadence, just as in our own time when judgement and treatment can be influenced by the excessive pressures of present-day drug advertising.

However, the fact remains that Egyptian medicine, as well as other forms of Egyptian culture, decayed as the centuries went on. To see it in its finest forms we must study its beginnings. Perhaps one of its main interests

4 *Ixora, an Indian deity*

lies in its nearness to, and effect on, Greek medicine. Moreover, because of the high degree of perfection reached in Egyptian embalming, it has been possible to study changes in the bones of mummies, giving the world a knowledge of some of the diseases that existed at that time.

Hebrew medicine

A study of the Old Testament will show that the Jewish writers held the opinion that disease was the direct result of wrongdoing and an expression of God's wrath. Healing only took place if the sufferers were worthy of cure and after prayers, atonement and sacrifice. As it was held that God conferred both health and disease, it is not surprising

to find that in the Bible there is little mention made of physicians.

In Old Testament times the Jews were a nomadic people and their great contribution to medicine has been their widespread distribution of a knowledge of personal and social hygiene. The methods they advocated and adopted to control epidemic disease and to maintain the general health of their community were of the greatest importance to the general development of medical science, not only at that time but also through the succeeding centuries.

Indian medicine

As the Hebrews were the pioneers and leaders in matters affecting public health, so

the ancient Hindus were for their time
outstanding in operative surgery.

In the earliest of Sanskrit writings, the
Rig Veda, which dates from about 1500 B.C.,
most of the medical information consists of
details of various spells and incantations.
Vedas (or Sacred Books) appearing later
contain much more medical information.

There are reports of hospitals being in
existence and mention is made of the
qualities necessary for a nurse or hospital
attendant. The medical uses of many drugs
were described, including at least two
(Henbane and Indian hemp) which were
employed quite extensively in the production
of certain degrees of anaesthesia. Possibly it
was this knowledge which at least partly
contributed to the amazing development of
surgery in the India of those days, when more
than one hundred and twenty surgical
instruments were used in the performance
of many different operations.

The attainment of such a degree of skill was
all the more amazing when it is remembered
how slight and distorted was the general
knowledge of anatomy. With the
Mohammedan conquest of India, Hindu
medicine declined, but the honour of being
pioneers in many forms of surgery will
always be theirs.

Chinese medicine

Although Chinese medicine has made
contributions which have demonstrated
ingenuity and originality, it has to all intents
and purposes remained absolutely stationary
for centuries. Several factors have
contributed towards this, such as the
persistence of the cult of the evil spirit or
demon in disease, the influence of ancestor
worship, which inevitably stresses the past
rather than the future, and a spirit of inertia
and fatalism encouraged by tradition and by
the various religions of the country.

The Chinese were the originators of
massage and perhaps the manipulation of
joints. They gave the world a knowledge of
certain very important drugs, and also of
acupuncture and the moxa. Acupuncture is
the pricking of certain areas of skin with
needles ; and moxas, possibly invented by
some early Chinese medical pyromaniac,
consist of little inflammable cones of material
which are placed on the body and then
ignited ! Both these methods of treatment
are forms of counter-irritation. This may be
defined as an artificial irritation produced in
one part of the body to act in opposition to,
and to remove, already existing irritation.

The mustard plaster and 'a good strong
liniment, please doctor' are present-day

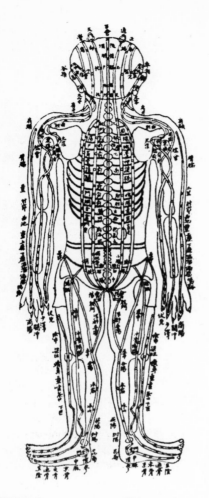

5 *Lines for acupuncture: a Chinese print*

examples of counter-irritation. Sken Ming, who lived about 3000 B.C., can probably be regarded as the father of Chinese medicine. An Emperor of China, who was also an able agriculturist, he was responsible for the development of the *Pen Tsao*, or Chinese *Materia Medica*. An English edition of this work was published in 1911, so it can be said that his work has already lasted for 5000 years.

18

Greek medicine

On a small rock-bound peninsula in the Mediterranean, some 2500 years ago, a handful of people brought new hope and new ambitions to the human race. It is hard to put into a few words what happened, but certain underlying principles gradually evolved. These were essentially that man was born to a noble purpose, to attain the highest possible physical, moral and intellectual development. Writing about this, Bertrand Russell says :[1]

'In all history nothing is so surprising or so difficult to account for as the sudden rise of civilization in Greece.

What they achieved in art and literature is familiar to everyone, but what they did in the purely intellectual realm is even more exceptional.'

Apollo

In view of this combination of passion and intellect, which enabled the Greeks to transform the world, it is particularly interesting to study the way in which Greek medicine evolved. Although its beginnings are obscured by myths and legends, there seems little doubt that knowledge derived

[1] Russell, Bertrand, *A History of Western Philosophy*, p 21, 1957.

6 *Statue of Asklepios in the Vatican Museum: note the snake emblem*

gods, killed Asklepios with a thunderbolt. Asklepios, who after all was the grandson of Zeus, then became a god and was worshipped all over Greece. The remains of his most important temple may be seen today at Epidaurus. Here an important medical school developed, and here also could be found the famous harmless yellow snakes that became associated with the teaching and worship of Asklepios.

Today the snake is still regarded as being a medical emblem. Temples dedicated to healing were presided over by priest-physicians who supervised both the ritual and the treatment. Although the familiar combination of religion and medicine still existed, other factors, which included psychotherapy[1] and physical medicine, began to play an increasingly important part in treatment.

As the years went on the influence of the early Greek philosophers became more and more obvious, and eventually, in 'the golden age of Pericles', following the decisive victories over the Persians, Greek civilisation reached its highest point.

Hippocrates
It was a fitting time for the birth of Hippocrates, the founder of scientific

from other cultures, for example those of Babylon, Egypt and India, played an important but unrecorded part in its development. The god of health and medicine was the sun-god, Apollo.

Tradition tells us that early in his life he established the shrine at Delphi which quite rapidly became not only famous but also the most sacred spot in all Greece. Apollo was reputed to have had a son, by name Asklepios, who lived about 1250 B.C. and was referred to by Homer as 'the blameless physician'.

Because of jealousy Zeus, father of the

[1] The treatment of mental or emotional disorders.

19

medicine. This remarkable man was born on the small island of Cos in 460 B.C.[1] It is unlikely that he was greatly influenced by the Asklepian principles of temple healing because the methods that he taught and followed were so very different.

Essentially the influence of Hippocrates was threefold. First, he taught that illnesses were due to natural causes and were not punishments for real or imaginary sins or due to evil spirits. Second, he sifted and simplified the work of existing medical schools, at the same time adorning them with the fruits of his own genius.

Third, he gave the medical profession the highest possible inspiration. He stressed the importance of considering the outlook (prognosis) of each case, and insisted on extreme accuracy in observation and in case histories.

His name is associated with the famous Hippocratic Oath which has been adopted as a code or pattern by doctors all over the world, and he was the author or inspiration of more than one hundred books which deal with his methods.

Here is a portion of the Hippocratic Oath.

'With purity and holiness I will pass my life and practice my Art . . . Into whatsoever

houses I enter I will go into them for the benefit of the sick and will abstain from every voluntary act of mischief and corruption.'

It is not hard to understand why the name of Hippocrates has always been held in reverence.

Aristotle and Theophrastus
Aristotle (384–322 B.C.), who was born about thirty years after the death of Hippocrates, was not only a famous philosopher but also the first great biologist. He laid the foundations of anatomy and embryology and dissected many animals. His thought and work influenced all science, particularly medicine. Aristotle was the tutor to Alexander the Great, but he also had many other pupils who later became famous.

One of these, Theophrastus (370–287 B.C.), laid the foundations of modern scientific botany. He described not only the natural history of plants, but also those plants that were used in the treatment of illness. With his death in 287 B.C. the period of decline in Greece commenced.

However, many aspects of Greek medicine, which reached its zenith with Hippocrates and his followers, flourished for four more centuries in the amazing Roman Empire.

[1] The date of Hippocrates' death is uncertain ; it may have been 335 B.C.

It must be remembered that, although we inherited from the Greeks a spirit of scientific enquiry, associated with a pure and disinterested form of medical practice, all Greek medicine was not of these high standards. The Greeks were also responsible for a far lower form of practice, which largely but not completely amounted to a form of charlatanism. This temple medical system is the antecedent of much of the medieval and modern medical hocus-pocus and quackery that has existed through the ages up to and including the present time.

Roman medicine

The medical system of Greece reached Rome slowly, when Greece was at the height of its power. Before that, Roman medicine was of a primitive order, influenced by folklore and divination. Many of the early Greek physicians in Rome were slaves and the status of the profession was low, remaining so until Julius Caesar in 46 B.C. gave to physicians full rights of Roman citizenship.

Roman genius found its full expression in measures likely to benefit public health. Roman houses were provided with sanitation and plumbing, the water being brought to the cities by aqueducts which conveyed it from storage areas many miles distant. Other achievements in hygiene included proper town planning and road making, central heating, warmed public baths and some control over the purity of foods.

The Romans were essentially a military people and in their wars of expansion cared for their wounded in hospitals, which become more widespread and scattered as the frontiers of the Empire became ever wider. It was in connection with the army that we see Roman medicine reach its highest level, but because of the general indifference to any form of theoretical science and the fact that the medical personnel ranked so much lower than the combatant officers, no contributions to knowledge were made by the Imperial Roman Army Medical Corps. Even at its best Roman medicine must be regarded as an inferior offshoot of Greek medicine to which it contributed very little. However, there were of course exceptions.

Galen
A great figure, whose work influenced medicine for over a thousand years, appeared in the Graeco-Roman period. This was Galen (A.D. 130–200), who was a talented but dogmatic teacher of great

21

diligence. He taught that the body was the vehicle of the soul, and this viewpoint satisfied both Christians and Moslems.[1] He acknowledged his indebtedness to both Hippocrates and Aristotle, but differed from the former in that he attempted to explain, by theoretical reasoning, what Hippocrates had worked out by painstaking observation and interpretation of facts. Because of the times in which he lived, because of his ingenuity and facility for explanation, and because of his mental stature, Galen became the final court of appeal.

However, there were three teachings of Galen which held back medical scientific development for centuries. The first concerned the doctrine of Vitalism which held that the blood became charged with certain essences, the highest of these being the 'Vital Spirit' which came from the brain. The second theory was that in its passage through the body, the blood passed from the right ventricle of the heart to the left ventricle through certain invisible pores in the wall between these two chambers. The third was associated with the treatment of wounds, claiming that the development of pus was an essential part of healing.

[1] Mohammed or Mahomet, founder of Mohammedanism or the Moslem religion, was born in about A.D. 570 and died in A.D. 632.

With the disintegration of the Roman Empire his work spread all over the civilised world. After his death medicine remained inert and lifeless and few advances occurred in the next 1400 years.

Christian Rome

Rome remained officially pagan until A.D. 335. In this year the persecution of the Christians, which had persisted for nearly 300 years, ceased when Christianity became the official religion of Rome. In some ways the early Christian Church impeded the progress of medical science. In efforts to detract nothing from the position of the one Great Physician, medicine was forced to take second place to the Church, emphasis being placed on prayer and fasting. The principles of Hippocrates were ignored and something equivalent to the underlying ideas of the Asklepian temple healing developed. This intolerance reached its climax in A.D. 391 when a mob of fanatics, allegedly under Christian influence, burnt to the ground the great library of Alexandria, which contained so much of the irreplaceable knowledge and wisdom of the pagan past. However, as Douglas Guthrie writes :[2]

'The infinite pity and patience expended by the Church upon the care of the sick far

[2] Guthrie, Douglas, *A History of Medicine*, p 85.

outweighs any temporary intolerance shown towards medicine. In addition it must not be forgotten that we are indebted to the medieval monks for the very existence of those ancient works which influenced and still influence the trend of medicine. By day and night the monk in his cell engaged in the work of translation and transcription, until eventually the invention of printing made learning available for all.'

Christianity brought to mankind new faith and hope and something for which to live. The gradual development of compassion towards weakness and suffering and the improvement in the status of women led to further hospital development and new departures in nursing. Probably the first of these Christian hospitals was established by Fabiola, a young Roman matron, who in A.D. 390 gave up her own home for this purpose. As these early Christian hospitals developed, they gradually combined within their walls orphanages and infirmaries. Thus they gave help not only to the sick but also to the aged and orphaned. By A.D. 400 hospitals had become part of the Church, being controlled and administered by bishops. A type of religious and semi-medical community life developed which was later called monasticism.

The downfall of Rome
When the last Roman Emperor was deposed in A.D. 476, the Western Empire ceased to exist, even in name. The disintegration of this vast empire left Europe practically nationless, mainly inhabited by loose tribal groups of varying size. As nations gradually developed from these larger groups, what survived of classical learning and science in Europe remained largely in monastic keeping. Speaking very generally, medicine then followed two divergent paths. One of these was that of monastic medicine, the beginnings of which have been described, and the other that of Arabian medicine.

Arabian medicine

Long after the death of Mohammed, the wild outlaw clans of Asia and Africa, which had helped in the formation of his empire, gradually developed and expanded into responsible nations. Unlike the early Christians, they revered the work and teaching of their predecessors and were tolerant of new thoughts and learning. It should be understood that the term 'Arab' or 'Arabian', used in reference to the medical leaders, authors and transcribers in this Mohammedan period, referred to the

7 *Early arabian surgery for spinal disorders*

language which they wrote and spoke and not necessarily to their religion or nationality. Many of these men were Christians, others were Jewish or Spanish. It is interesting to note that Jews under Arabian domination were not persecuted as they were in so many other places following their dispersal from Palestine.

The main contributions of Arabian medicine were made in the fields of pharmacology and chemistry. Many new drugs were developed and introduced, and descriptions of these, together with methods of preparation, persisted throughout the Middle Ages.

Great doctors came to the fore from time to time during this period. Probably the most noted was a Persian known as Avicenna (980–1036). His most famous work was the *Canon Medicinae*. This vast collection of medical knowledge came to be used as the main textbook until the seventeenth century, not only in the Arabic world but also in the Latin West. However, on the debit side of the ledger a most regrettable and fundamental error developed in the thinking of the medical personnel of these times. Galen had strongly held the idea that surgery was only a rather indifferent method of treatment, forgetting or ignoring the Hippocratic dictum that surgery was 'the very

24

right hand of medicine'.

To add to this, as a famous medical historian[1] has put it, 'The Arabian commentators of Galen and their copyists were obsessed with the idea, peculiar to oriental religions, that it is unclean or unholy to touch the human body with the hands.' Christians, on the other hand, taught that the body was sacred and should not be defaced by active surgical measures. All this resulted in the divorce of medicine from surgery and so often forced the latter into the hands of the untrained, the uneducated and the charlatan.

By the end of the thirteenth century the light of the vast Moslem Empire was becoming dimmed and the great days of Arabian medicine were drawing to a close. Five hundred years after the fall of Rome, the best attributes of Arabian and monastic medicine fused in the formation of the famous School of Salerno.

[1] Garrison, F. H., *An Introduction to the History of Medicine*, 4th ed., p 144, 1929.

3 The medieval period *c.* 1100–1438

It is difficult to give names to periods in the world's history because such divisions are so often artificial, obviously having no clear-cut beginning or ending in terms of time. That is why such eras often overlap and intertwine. The early medieval period was largely taken up with the evolution of social units from the scattered chaos which resulted from the downfall of Rome. Along with the emergence of these social units occurred the development of feudalism and ecclesiasticism. When one remembers the effects of the last World War on so many races and peoples, it is not difficult to understand the appeal of the Christian Church and monastic life to the distressed, uncertain and homeless of those times. Monasteries developed all over Europe and the first Crusade, stimulated by religious zeal and developing nationalism, started in 1095.

This was an era when original thought was under the ban of authority and intellectual freedom was controlled by Church and State. Often it was actually unsafe to hold opinions that deviated from the official line (there is a modern parallel here). Enormous amounts of mental energy and time were spent in fruitless and obscure reasoning, and for all practical purposes experimental science in any form ceased to exist. Because of this, medicine sank to a low level and remained in a state of stagnation until the Renaissance. However, as always there were brilliant exceptions to this state of affairs. Fortunately it is the function of the historian to record the activities of the exceptions rather than dwell on the state of stagnation.

The School of Salerno

Medical learning and teaching became established on a sound basis at the little seaside town of Salerno near Naples. According to legend, this first organised medical school in Europe had four founders, a Jew, a Roman, a Greek and an Arab. Such a legend could well be true because the Salernian school was a secular institution in a sea of monasticism. It was open to all, regardless of race or religion. It started sometime in the ninth century and reached its peak after the Norman conquest of the town in 1076. The conquering Norman knight, Duke Robert Guiscard, made the town his capital and from then it became a wealthy centre of trade, education and culture.

Two of the most famous figures whose work added lustre to the School of Salerno were surgeons. The writings of Roger of Palermo and his pupil Roland of Parma became standard surgical textbooks, which

for centuries were considered classics.
However, they regarded suppuration and the
slow delayed union of wounds by what is
known as 'second intention', as an essential
feature in wound healing. This of course was
quite in line with the teachings of Galen and
was the generally held view of the times.

Wound healing and 'laudable pus'

If the edges of a wound are brought
together, the injured part kept at rest and the
entry of organisms (germs or microbes) into
the wound prevented, primary union with
minimal scar-formation will occur in a few
days. If such a wound becomes infected, one
of two things will happen. The body will
mobilise its defences and the white
corpuscles in the blood-stream will
encircle, engulf and eventually destroy the
invaders. The wastage from this battle will
show itself in a purulent discharge, of the
type that the medieval (and not so
medieval) surgeon referred to as 'laudable
pus'. On the other hand, if the invading
organisms gain the upper hand, they spread
and multiply with great rapidity. The battle
then is one-sided, there is usually little or no
discharge and blood-poisoning ensues. The
wounded person's life is then in great danger.

26

For obvious reasons, therefore, it is not
surprising to find the medieval surgeon
almost welcoming the presence of pus. It
then only needed some *de facto* reasoning,
the closing of eyes on the wound that very
occasionally healed by primary union, and
the teaching that pus was desirable or
'laudable' was established.

This idea, first taught by Galen, adversely
influenced the progress of surgery for
centuries.

In view of all this it is remarkable to find
two surgeons trained at Salerno, Hugh of
Lucca and his son Theodoric, advocating the
dry (aseptic) treatment of wounds, and
writing as follows.

'For it is not necessary, as Roger and
Roland have written . . . that pus should be
generated in wounds. Such a practice is
indeed to hinder nature and to prolong the
disease'.

Alas, the influence of Galen was too strong,
and until the time of Lister only de
Mondeville, Paracelsus and perhaps Paré
upheld these ideas and questioned the
principle of 'laudable pus'.

In the twentieth century many people are
only too well aware of the devastating
effects of the acceptance of a false ideology.
The human race always pays for its mistakes
in full, and there is no doubt that the idea that

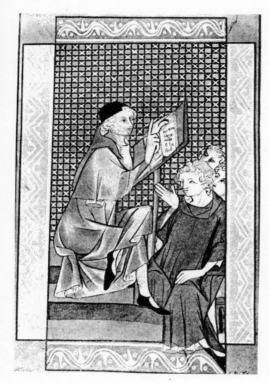

8 *Henri de Mondeville lecturing: 'No surgeon can be expert who does not know medicine'*

suppuration was essential to healing was a dreadful mistake, the price of which was death and suffering persisting for centuries.

Henri de Mondeville (1260–1320) and the School of Montpellier

The twelfth and thirteenth centuries saw the establishment of several medieval universities, including Montpellier (1181). In association with this university arose a famous medical school which challenged the authority of Salerno. Other well-known medieval schools were developed at

Naples, Palermo and later Paris. Henri De Mondeville, lecturer in anatomy at Montpellier, was an advanced surgeon who, like his teacher Theodoric, strongly advocated cleanliness and dryness in the treatment of wounds. He wrote a surgical treatise full of sound common-sense and trenchant observations. Some of the latter were as follows :

'God did not exhaust all his creative power in making Galen.

Many more surgeons know how to cause suppuration than to heal a wound.

It is dangerous for a surgeon to operate in any way different to the method in common use.

No surgeon can be expert who does not know medicine, just as no one can be a good physician if he is ignorant of surgery.'

This last observation is as true today as it was when it was first uttered.

Another famous figure in French medicine, Guy de Chauliac (1300–68), educated at Montpellier, Paris and Bologna, became the best-known surgeon of his day. He wrote extensively and in his works is found a detailed description of the medieval substitute for anaesthesia, the narcotic or soporific sponge. This sponge was seeped in such drugs as opium, mandragora, hyoscyamus and henbane. Fumes from it were supposed to be inhaled, but probably its main action depended on at least part of the contents of the sponge being swallowed.

Although a man of wide education and high principles, he opposed the teachings of Theodoric and de Mondeville in the matter of the treatment of wounds. Because of his great reputation he thus unconsciously played his part in delaying the progress of surgery by centuries.

English medicine in medieval times

Before the Norman conquest, English medicine was at a very low ebb. Probably the earliest organised healers were the Druids, who were a body of priestly magicians specialising in second sight, sorcery, sacrifice and herb lore. They were followed by the Anglo-Saxon leeches whose knowledge was perhaps a little better but whose status was definitely lower. The care of the sick and wounded was largely in the hands of women and this state of affairs persisted until after the Norman conquest, when increased educational facilities gradually became available to physicians and priests.

The earliest of a long line of English surgeons was John of Arderne (1306–90).

He was an army surgeon who gained immense experience during the Hundred Years' War. He wrote extensively and his surgical writings influenced English surgery for nearly 200 years.

The greatest experimenter of the thirteenth century was Roger Bacon. He was a Franciscan monk who was educated at Oxford. H. G. Wells[1] describes him as an Englishman who was irritable, hasty, honest and shrewd and at least two centuries ahead of his world. Although he was not a physician he must have influenced medicine by continually insisting on the necessity and value of experimentation as opposed to argument and the blind acceptance of ancient dictums. He wrote extensively about optics and uses for convex lenses. He has been credited with the invention of spectacles and gunpowder, and his writings contain forecasts of aviation and mechanical transport both by sea and land.

Medieval hospitals

The most important achievement of medieval medicine lay in the development of hospitals and the care of the sick. This was

[1] Wells, H. G., *The Outline of History*, p 479, The Waverly Book Company.

28

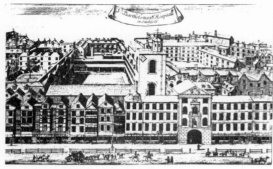

9 *St Bartholomew's Hospital 1720*

largely due to the work of the Church. The Emperor Constantine[1] closed by decree the pagan Greek temples (*Asklepieia*) and the Roman hospitals were mainly military organisations. The Arabian hospitals, some of which were large and important, started long after many Christian hospitals had been established and probably adopted the idea from them. The credit for doing on a large scale something practical to relieve human sufferings and misfortune must be given to Christianity. One of the first of these medieval hospitals was built by the Knights Hospitallers of St John of Jerusalem on the island of Rhodes. They settled there and also in Cyprus after the capture of Jerusalem by the Saracens in 1187.

In 1530 they moved to Malta which they held until 1798. Although greatly changed, the order still continues in Rome, and an English offshoot undertakes hospital and first-aid work mainly through the St John's Ambulance Association. This Association still wears as part of its uniform the eight-pointed Maltese Cross which was worn in medieval times on the black robes of the knights.

The oldest British hospital of size existing today is St Bartholomew's, which was founded in 1123 by Rahere, once minstrel and jester in the Court of Henry I.

Rahere was a remarkable man. Kipling[2] in a fascinating story writes, 'We were all—the King not least—overborne by that terrible scarlet, and black wizard-jester.' Rahere apparently had considerable influence over Henry, because when he formed a religious order he was given a grant of land on which the hospital was built.

St Thomas's Hospital is the second oldest hospital in Britain. It was started in 1215. Gradually the control of hospitals passed from the Church to the municipalities, and they became lay institutions.

Plagues and epidemic diseases

'In the Middle Ages European humanity was plagued with epidemic diseases as never before or since.'[3] Looking back it is possible to see many of the reasons for this. The crowded, filthy and unsanitary conditions which existed in walled medieval towns, and

---

[1] Constantine (A.D. 274–337), first Christian Emperor of Rome and founder of Constantinople.

[2] Kipling, Rudyard, *Rewards and Fairies—The Tree of Justice*, 1910 ed. p 333.

[3] Garrison, F. H., *History of Medicine*, 4th ed., p 186, 1929.

29

the general state of immorality and squalor resulting from constant wars, oppression and ignorance, were important factors.

The first of these great medieval epidemics was leprosy, which in the early centuries of the Christian era spread into Europe from Asia. The contagious nature of this disease had long been recognised, and the treatment of the leper in medieval times was unbelievably callous. He was literally banished from human society and was declared legally dead. In the course of time these cruel measures took effect and Europe gradually became free from leprosy. Because of the success of this policy, a number of other diseases which became recognised as infectious were treated by the same restrictive methods.

The most dreadful of these medieval plagues was the Black Death, which attacked the civilised world in the fourteenth century, killing about a quarter of the population. In this awful epidemic at least half the people in London perished.

However, there were instances where the public health measures of the day successfully kept these terrible plagues at bay. These measures included drastic restrictions and regulations designed to prevent infected persons or infected food and drink from entering cities.

The Republic of Ragusa on the Adriatic Sea established bases outside the city and the harbour where newly arrived people were forced to spend a period of time in open air and sunlight. Eventually forty days of isolation were found to be necessary and this period was referred to as the *Quarantina*. From this developed our modern word 'quarantine'.

Eventually epidemics of plague ceased in Europe, a result not so much of these restrictions as of the extermination of the black rat by the brown. The actual organisms or germs which cause plague are carried by fleas which come mainly from the black rat. The actual plague organisms were not isolated until 1894.

Another terrible disease of the Middle Ages was syphilis. It was said to have been introduced into Europe from the New World by the sailors of Christopher Columbus. For a long time its various methods of infection were not properly understood and the disease spread far and wide, devastating and degenerating the human race.

Astrology

This was the so-called art or science of foretelling the future from the positions of the stars. The origins of the belief that the health and fortunes of men and indeed nations are controlled and influenced by movements of the stars and planets are so remote as to antedate all written records. Man with his love of magic studied astrology in every European nation, and in Egypt, India, China, Arabia, Babylonia and Assyria. Astrology has left us with a legacy of words. People are referred to as being saturnine, jovial, martial or mercurial, and in medicine we have invented the words lunacy and venereal disease. To be moonstruck is undesirable, but it is undoubtedly a good thing to be born under a lucky star !

Astrology began to decay at the time of the Renaissance and languished in the seventeenth century. Kipling[1] in a most interesting story describes the attempts of Nicholas Culpeper, herbalist and astrologer, to control an outbreak of plague in a village in England during the Civil War. The dread effects of the disease are described, and treatment based on astrology, folklore and common sense is carried out with eventual success.

[1] Kipling, Rudyard, *Rewards and Fairies—A Doctor of Medicine*, 1910 ed., p 253.

4 The period of the Renaissance

This period, which commenced about the end of the fourteenth century, resulted in drastic changes in the outlook of thinking men. Italy was the birthplace of the movement, and many forces operated in gradually liberating men from the disciplines imposed by Church and State on freedom of speech and thought. The inventions of gunpowder and printing, and the discovery of America were the most potent of these forces. The first sounded the knell of feudalism, the second gave promise of widespread education and the third enlarged the scope and extent of the known world.

This spirit of enlightenment reached England at the beginning of that remarkable period known as the Elizabethan Age. It is fashionable today, when considering the factors which make history, to pay particular attention to trends in ideas and movements, and less to the individual and to isolated incidents. However, to trace an idea, an experiment or a technique from earliest beginnings, one must study the relevant individuals. This is particularly necessary in the history of medicine which is essentially the story of men with ideas.

The year 1543 marks a peak in the history of medicine and of science, because in that year Nicholas Copernicus[1] revolutionised astronomy and Andreas Vesalius rendered a similar service to medicine by his work on anatomy.

Anatomists of the Renaissance

Two great artists of this period learnt anatomy by breaking with tradition and practising dissection well before the teachers of anatomy did so. They were Leonardo da Vinci (1452–1519) and Michelangelo Bounarroti (1475–1564), who pursued these studies at considerable risk to themselves.

Leonardo da Vinci, who was centuries ahead of his time in the field of original ideas, made several important anatomical discoveries and left to posterity hundreds of anatomical sketches of great worth and beauty. He started his studies in anatomy as an aid to accurate painting of the human figure, but soon the desire to know, to discover, and to understand became all important. Although he has now been accepted as being one of the very first of a long line of experimental scientists, it is

[1] Nicholas Copernicus (1473–1543), a founder of modern astronomy, proved that the sun is the centre of our universe.

32

sometimes thought that, because his drawings and notes were lost for centuries, he played little or no part in assisting Vesalius and other anatomists of the Renaissance. However, this view has been challenged, notably by Singer,[1] who writes: 'But the atmosphere created by Leonardo and the other great artist anatomists did certainly bear fruit. The naturalistic movement in art which Leonardo represented had the profoundest influence on anatomy. Without it the subsequent work of Vesalius would have been impossible.'

Michelangelo claimed that his knowledge of human anatomy helped him not only artistically but also architecturally in that great monument to his genius, the dome of St Peter's.[2]

Vesalius

Andreas Vesalius (1514–64) occupied a position of special greatness in the history of medicine. He made anatomy a living, working science. His famous book[3] swept aside a whole host of Galenic and other beliefs and superstitions. Among the beliefs to disappear for ever were those of Adam's missing rib, a mysterious bone called *Luz* (a relic of Jewish mythology), and, in the second edition of the *Fabrica* in 1555, the pores in the septum between the ventricles of the heart. This last denial of Galen's idea was particularly important because it was one of the fundamental points on which Harvey based his work on the circulation of the blood. Inevitably the person who sweeps away the beliefs of the past, no matter how wrong they may be, is the victim of bitter criticism and controversy. This was the fate that overtook Vesalius. He bowed before the storm and at the end of only three years his great work was over. He resigned his Professorship in Surgery and Anatomy at the University of Padua and became Court Physician at Madrid. He died in 1564 at the age of fifty.

The extent of his work and that of his associates and followers was so vast that its true significance and value to surgical development was only slowly appreciated.

[1] Singer, Charles, *A short history of Anatomy and Physiology from the Greeks to Harvey*, Dover ed., 1957.
[2] Stone, Irving, *The Agony and the Ecstasy*, pp 190–204, Collins, 1961. A biographical novel of Michelangelo.
[3] *De Humani Corporis Fabrica* (On the Fabric of the Human Body), generally known as the *Fabrica*.

3

Surgery in the Renaissance

Mention has been made of capable work done by surgeons in medieval times. However, the invention of gunpowder greatly increased mankind's capacity to kill and maim, and naturally provided an increased demand for army surgeons.

The greatest surgeon of the Renaissance was Ambroise Paré (1510–90). After lowly beginnings and some training in the great Paris Hospital, the *Hôtel Dieu*, he became an army surgeon. Exhibiting courage, ability, common sense and above all humanity, he rapidly rose to the forefront. Probably the greatest of his many contributions to surgery was in the treatment of gunshot wounds. The universal view of such wounds was that they were poisoned burns requiring as soon as possible an application of boiling oil ! On one occasion following a grim battle, Paré's supply of boiling oil gave out and he was forced to use simple dressings.[1] After spending a worrying night, he was amazed to find in the morning that the soldiers whose wounds had been dressed with simple lotions were comparatively comfortable, while those on whom the boiling oil had been used were feverish and in great pain. Thus he discovered that

[1] 'A digestive of eggs, oil of roses and turpentine.'

gunshot wounds were not poisoned, and that boiling oil was not only unnecessary but actually cruel and harmful.

Paré introduced many new surgical instruments and operative procedures : massage, artificial limbs and eyes ; and he was the first to suggest that flies were possible transmitters of infectious disease. A casual reader of this book may think, after skimming through this greatly condensed list of Paré's achievements, that claims made for his greatness are perhaps exaggerated. It is suggested that any such doubter think back some 400 years and imagine that he is lying on a battlefield, wounded and in pain, waiting in dread for the greater agony of the boiling oil. Paré then might have seemed to be the greatest man in the world (which in fact he well might have been). Engraved on a statue erected to his memory and honour are his famous words :

'*I dressed him, God healed him.*'

Paracelsus and medicine

One of the most controversial figures in medicine at this period was the man who was known as Paracelsus (1490–1541). He was the son of a Swiss country doctor, and, after attending the University of Basel, travelled for twelve years over most parts of Europe. Returning to Basel in 1526 he was appointed lecturer in medicine, at that University. Many differing opinions are held about this man's place in medical history. He has been described by some as a braggart and a drunken charlatan and by others as the most original thinker of the sixteenth century. From his full name, Aureolus Theophrastus Bombastus von Hohenheim, was evolved the word 'bombastic'. There is little doubt that he was intolerant, aggressive and boastful. Before he started his lectures in Basel he publicly burned the works of Galen and Avicenna, announcing that his shoe-buckles knew more than these writers !

He lectured in German instead of Latin and in general condemned a great deal of what his contemporaries believed. At a time when gross departures from accepted lines of thought and action were still fraught with risks, he declared war on the superstitions of the past and the medical complacency that went with them. He attacked witchcraft and the wandering charlatans who claimed surgical training and knowledge which they did not possess. He greatly advanced the knowledge of drugs, simplified prescription and introduced mineral baths as a method of treatment. Although in many ways he advanced medicine by fighting about it, his behaviour, which was not calculated to win friends and favourably influence people, was eventually his undoing. He was forced to leave Basel and continue his wandering. He eventually acquired a remarkable reputation, practising and teaching in many European cities. He died in Salzburg in 1541.[1]

Thomas Linacre and the Royal College of Physicians of London

Thomas Linacre (1460–1524) was educated at Oxford. He became court physician to three successive sovereigns. Probably his greatest achievement was in organising a body to control the practice of medicine. This was very necessary because medicine was then largely practised by untrained monks, wandering quacks and charlatans, and self-appointed specialists, as well as by trained physicians. Henry VIII, who was then King of England, granted a charter in 1518 to a small body of graduate physicians. Linacre was the first President of this body which, as the Royal College of Physicians of London, was granted power to examine candidates and license physicians.

[1] See Robert Browning's poem, *Paracelsus*.

Michael Servetus
and the pulmonary circulation

Michael Servetus (1509–53) is claimed by some to be one of the greatest men of his age, whose genius enabled him to understand and correlate a great range of natural phenomena. He published an account of the pulmonary circulation in a theological work in which he also referred to the Trinity as a three-headed monster. He was unwise enough to send a copy of his book to Calvin, whom he regarded as a religious reformer with views as advanced as his own. He was condemned for heresy and burned alive in Geneva on 27th October 1553, together with his works. The relevant and remarkable passage from his book *Restoration of Christianity* is as follows :

'The vital spirit is generated from the mixture in the lungs of the inspired air with the subtly elaborated blood which the right ventricle sends to the left. The communication between the ventricles, however, is not made through the mid-wall of the heart, but in a wonderful way the fluid blood is conducted by a long detour from the right ventricle through the lungs, where it is acted on by the lungs and becomes red in colour, passes from the arteria venosa into the vena artercosa, whence it is finely drawn by diastole into the left ventricle.'

In fairness to Calvin it must be remembered that the year was 1553 and that according to some historians Calvin did try unsuccessfully to have the method of execution altered.

5 The seventeenth century

The seventeenth century was an age of intense intellectual activity and scientific discovery. Gradually observation and experiment became the accepted method of attack on nature's secrets. What had happened to men like Servetus, Sir Thomas More, Galileo, Copernicus and so many others, in the long run helped not to strengthen but to loosen the bonds of Church and State. As a result of these new freedoms, individualism flourished. With such developments some of the good things of the old order gradually disappeared, such as good hospital management, care of the sick and organised nursing.

William Harvey and the circulation of the blood

The greatest name in seventeenth century medicine was William Harvey (1578–1657). He was educated at Cambridge and Padua. At the latter university he was influenced by the work of Fabricus ab Aquapendente, a prominent name in the series of famous anatomists who had succeeded Vesalius. Fabricus wrote a book about certain valves that occur in veins. He described them, but at that point his thinking stopped. The influence of Galen was too strong for him to go further, but his pupil, Harvey, possessed the right kind of mind and the capacity to realise quite early in his work that the circulation of the blood must be a continuous movement in one direction. Eventually, by experimental dissections, ligations, and the injection of fluids into the blood-vessels, he came to see that the same blood that is pumped into and transmitted by the arteries away from the heart returns to the heart by the veins.

In 1628 he published what was probably the most famous book in medical literature. This small book of seventy-two pages had a long title. It was called *Exercitatio Anatomica De Motu Cordis et Sanguinis in Animalibus.*[1]

Although Harvey was able to prove that the blood circulated, he was unable to show that channels existed between the smallest arteries and veins. Harvey had no microscope and was unable to demonstrate the capillary anastomosis. The existence of this extensive network of minute vessels was first described by a famous early micro-scopist, Marcello Malpighi of Bologna, thirty-three years after Harvey first published his great work.

The understanding of the circulation of the blood was the basis of a new interest in

[1] *The Anatomical Treatise on the Movement of the Heart and Blood,* generally known as *De Motu Cordis*.

11 *Harvey demonstrating to Charles I his theory of the circulation of the blood*

physiology. No true advance was possible without this knowledge. Harvey, therefore, must be remembered not only as one of the great figures of medicine, but also as the father of modern physiology.

Robert Boyle and the Oxford scientists

Although Harvey was able to demonstrate so clearly how the blood circulated, he gave no explanation why this occurred. This problem was eventually solved by the work of four young Oxford scientists led by Robert Boyle (1627–91). These men were satisfied that

the only way in which truths could be discovered was by methods of deduction based on observation and experimentation. Probably their most important work was done in the field of chemistry which they made into an independent science, freeing it forever from the uncertain mysticism of alchemy.

Boyle, who was one of the founders of the Royal Society,[1] is also remembered because of his famous law relating to the compressibility of gases. He and his associates investigated the mechanisms of respiration and showed that air was necessary for life and for combustion.

[1] The Royal Society was founded in 1660.

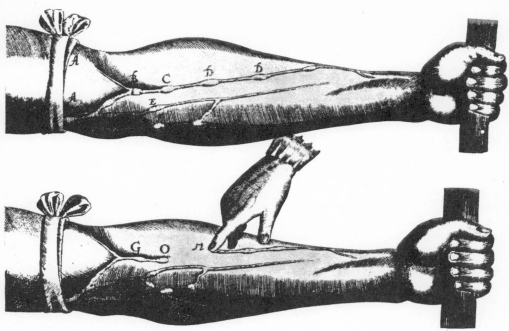

12 *Woodcuts from* De Motu Cordis

Contributions towards an understanding of the interaction, which takes place in the lungs, of the air with the blood, were made by Hooke, Lower and Mayow.[1] The latter suspected the presence in the air of the substance we know as oxygen.[2] It is also interesting to record that Robert Hooke (1635–1703) was also a microscopist of note and curator to the newly formed Royal Society. He was the first to see and illustrate a plant cell under his microscope.

[1] Young Oxford scientists who, together with Boyle, were among the founders of the Royal Society.
[2] Oxygen, isolated by Priestly (1774) and named by Lavoisier.

Thomas Sydenham, the English Hippocrates

It was in the seventeenth century that medicine first showed signs of becoming what it is today, a complex, many-sided technological profession.[3] With the acquisition of new skills and knowledge, there is always the possibility that other important aspects of medical practice will

[3] The discussion which has gone on for years as to whether medicine is an art or a science has never achieved much, and nowadays tends to be regarded as being rather tedious. The future status of medicine will depend on whether enough doctors can be trained to practise the new medicine and yet preserve the old art and tradition of service.

39

become forgotten or overlooked. There is always the danger that methods can become more important than mankind and the disease more than the patient.

In the seventeenth century with its spate of new physiological and experimental work and all the excitement that went with it, that danger obviously existed. One of the greatest physicians of the age, Thomas Sydenham (1624–89), turned his back on medical theorising and experimentation and went back to the Hippocratic methods of observation and experience. Sydenham taught that it was at the bedside and only at the patient's bedside that disease could be studied first-hand and observation made and experience developed.

In treatment he used simple remedies. He was one of the first to use iron preparations for anaemia and cinchona bark (containing quinine) from Peru in the treatment of malaria. Malaria or ague was a prevalent and serious disease in seventeenth century England. The favourite teaching regarding the cause of such fevers was that of the 'miasma'. It was thought that decaying material, infected wounds or persons, marshy grounds and the like, gave off noxious gaseous substances capable of causing disease. The name malaria perpetuates this idea : *mal aria*, bad air.

Sydenham probably agreed with this theory because he was a great advocate of fresh air in sick rooms. He was able to distinguish between scarlet fever and measles, and he wrote treatises on hysteria and chorea.

As a teacher of medicine he was unrivalled, and his influence lasted not only in England but also in Europe for more than a century. It was said that Boerhaave, a famous teacher of medicine at the University of Leyden, of whom we shall hear more later, always raised his hat when he mentioned Sydenham's name during his lectures.

The beginnings of medicine in the New World

The development of settlements on the North American continent quite soon attracted emigrant physicians from Europe, mainly from England and Holland. The oldest educational institution and senior university of America, Harvard, was founded in 1636, and the College of William and Mary in Virginia in 1693. As educational facilities slowly developed, more and more students were trained at home, but for a great many years students and practitioners made the long journey to

European centres to further their medical education.

The rapid growth of the country, the vast distances involved and the small number of adequately trained doctors, were factors responsible for the development of a type of practical and self-reliant practitioner prepared to tackle any emergency which came to hand.

The first hospital in the New World was established in Mexico City by Cortez in 1524, the second in Quebec in 1639 and the third in Montreal in 1644. The name of Jeanne Mance,[1] a young Frenchwoman, is indissolubly linked with this hospital. After this time, until the middle of the nineteenth century, the profession of nursing sank to an extremely low level. This long period of over 150 years has been referred to as the 'Dark Age of Nursing'.

The passing of
the seventeenth century

Although the seventeenth century was a most fruitful period of intense intellectual activity and experimental medicine, a veritable golden age, it was nevertheless a period of transition. The practical application of new discoveries and new methods is always delayed, but because of poor communications and the natural resistance towards change, the time-lag in the seventeenth and early eighteenth centuries was marked. The following extracts from John Aubrey (1626–1669), the author of *Brief Lives*, will give us an idea of medical practice in those times. Aubrey had the gift of condensing a great deal into a few words. This is what he writes about a Dr William Butler (d. 1618) whom he refers to as 'the Greatest Physitian of his time'.[2]

'The Dr lyeing at the Savoy in London next the waterside where there was a Balcony look't into the Thames, a patient came to him that was greviously tormented with an Ague. The Dr orders a boate to be in readinesse under his windowe and discoursed with the patient (a Gent.) in the balcony, when on a signal given, two or three lusty fellows came behind the gentleman and threw him a matter of 20 feet into the Thames. This surprise absolutely cured him.
    Again,
    'A Gent. with a red ugly pumpled face came to him for a cure. Said the Dr, I must hang you. So presently he had a device made

[1] *The Story of Nursing*, 4th revised edition, p 49.

[2] *Aubrey's Brief Lives*, ed. Oliver Lawson Dick, a Peregrine book, p 149.

ready to hang him from a beame in the roome, and when he was e'en almost dead he cut the veines that fed these pumples and let out the black ugley bloud and cured him.'

These seem drastic treatments for what were probably malaria and acne. Two observations can be made. The first is that it is improbable that Dr Butler would know if his patients were permanently cured. It is most unlikely that he would ever see them again. The second observation can probably be made in any century, and it is simply that there are no 'good old days' as far as medicine is concerned.

6 Medicine in the eighteenth century

The brightest star of the eighteenth century, perhaps of all time, was Sir Isaac Newton (1642–1727). Although he was not directly concerned with medicine, the vast scope of his work and vision and his concept that certain fixed laws governed not only earthly matters but also the whole of the universe, had far-reaching effects on all sciences. The eighteenth century has been referred to by medical historians as a period of consolidation in which the accumulated products of the research and new thought of the past two hundred years were sifted, brought into some sort of order and then utilised to the best advantage. It was found that the clear and logical thinking of Newton and his followers, when applied to other sciences, helped to bring order out of chaos.

Boerhaave and his pupils

A great medical figure in the earlier part of the eighteenth century was Hermann Boerhaave (1668–1738). He was appointed a teacher at the University of Leyden in 1701. This University, which was the first to establish teaching at the bedside in its medical school, gained added lustre from Boerhaave's appointment, because he became quite quickly the greatest clinical teacher of the century and attracted students to Leyden from all parts of the world. He was a man of wide learning, culture and humanity, but probably his greatest gift was his capacity to inspire into his pupils and co-workers an intense desire for knowledge and progress.

Singer[1] writes thus of Boerhaave:

'To him the debt of British medicine and through it of British well-being is quite incalculable. Through his pupils he is the real founder of the Edinburgh Medical School, and through it of the best medical teaching in the English-speaking countries of the world.'

One of the greatest of Boerhaave's pupils was the Swiss Albrecht von Haller (1708–77) whose special distinction was as a physiologist. His most important contributions were concerned with the action of the central nervous system and certain characteristics of muscle. He influenced physiological thinking for at least a hundred years and was also eminent as an anatomist, a botanist and a medical · historian.

[1] Singer, Charles, *A Short History of Medicine*, 1928, p 140.

Scottish medicine and surgery

The Edinburgh School of Surgery may be traced back to the year 1505. It was then that the surgeons and barbers, who had recently been formed into a corporation, presented a petition to the Town Council requesting permission to dissect the bodies of executed criminals, so that they might gain anatomical knowledge. This was rather remarkable, and, to put it into some sort of perspective, it must be remembered that the father of anatomy, Vesalius, was still unborn and that thirty-five years had to elapse before the English Company of Barber-Surgeons was chartered.

In Edinburgh the surgeons were legally separated from the barbers in 1722. In 1662 Sir Robert Sibbald (1641–1722) returned to Edinburgh from Leyden. He founded in 1681 the Royal College of Physicians of Edinburgh —and became first Professor of Medicine in the College (later the University) of Edinburgh.

Another famous physician who attained professorial status was Dr Archibald Pitcairne (1652–1713). At one time Pitcairne was Professor of Medicine at Leyden where Boerhaave was one of his pupils. Another pupil was John Monro who nourished the ambition to make Edinburgh a world centre of medical education. To further this aim he arranged for his son to have an extensive medical education first in Edinburgh, later in Leyden under Boerhaave and finally in London under the famous English surgeon Cheselden.[1]

Returning to Edinburgh, Alexander Monro was appointed Professor of Anatomy in 1720. Although he was only twenty-two years of age when he took up the appointment, he was very successful and developed a great reputation as an anatomist and a teacher. He was succeeded in 1758 by his son, also Alexander, named Secundus, and he in turn by his son, Alexander Monro, Tertius. Thus, what may be termed the Monro dynasty lasted for a period of 126 years. During the first seventy years of that period some 12,800 students were taught. The success of the Monros stimulated four Fellows of the Edinburgh College of Physicians (also pupils of Boerhaave's) to apply for professorships at the University. In the same year (1726) the first chair of midwifery was founded, and, when the Infirmary was opened in 1741, the Edinburgh Medical School was firmly established. To quote Guthrie,[2]

[1] William Cheselden (1688–1752), surgeon to St Thomas's Hospital ; a remarkably dexterous and rapid operator in an age when speed was essential.
[2] Guthrie, Douglas, A History of Medicine, 1946, p 225.

44

13 *William Hunter: 'He worked till he dropped and lectured when he was dying'*

'The torch of learning which had been lit in Greece passed to Salerno, then to Montpellier and Padua, then to Leyden, and early in the eighteenth century was handed on to Edinburgh, which then became the centre of medical learning.'

The Glasgow Medical School and William Hunter
The founder of the Glasgow School of Medicine was William Cullen (1710–90).

He was a pupil of Monro Primus. During his life he occupied chairs in medicine and chemistry at both Glasgow and Edinburgh. He lectured at the latter University until he was seventy-eight years of age. He was one of the first to lecture in his native tongue and he was a devoted teacher who inspired his students. One of his pupils who achieved

fame was William Hunter (1718–83). He came to London and became a leading obstetrician. He also established a famous school of anatomy in Great Windmill Street, where the leading anatomists and surgeons of the period, including his famous brother John, were trained. Stephen Paget, quoted by Garrison,[1] gives us a verbal picture of William Hunter, worthy of Aubrey :

'He never married, he had no country house, he looks in his portraits a fastidious, fine gentleman ; but he worked till he dropped and lectured when he was dying.'

His famous collection of anatomical specimens is now housed in the Hunterian museum at Glasgow University.

[1] Garrison, Fielding H., *An Introduction to the History of Medicine*, 1929, p 339.

14 *John Hunter: 'He alone made us gentlemen'*

John Hunter

John Hunter (1728–93) was the greatest
figure in eighteenth century surgery. He was
educated partly by his brother and partly by
the celebrated Percival Pott[1] of St
Bartholomew's Hospital. His energy was
amazing and his activities incredible. He did
original work on tendon repair after injury,
on inflammation, teeth, wound healing and
shock, and evolved an operation to deal with
large pulsating swellings of the arteries,
known as aneurisms. Most of these were
complications of long-standing syphilis. In
those days aneurisms were quite common
and nearly always proved eventually fatal.
Before John Hunter's time, educated
surgeons based their work mainly on
anatomy, having little knowledge of
pathology, the study of the morbid

[1] Pott, Percival (1714–88) : he described fracture of the
fibula (Pott's fracture) and tuberculous disease of
the spine (Pott's disease).

conditions present in disease. It was
Hunter's greatest achievement that he
realised and taught the importance of
applying the available knowledge to
surgery after having verified experimentally
the accuracy of his conclusions. He raised
surgery from a craft to the level of an
experimental science. What he did for the
social status of the surgeon is indicated by a
remark attributed to one of his colleagues :

'He alone made us gentlemen.'

After many years of very hard work he
acquired a magnificent collection of
specimens illustrating not only human
anatomy but also the comparative anatomy
of animals, birds and insects. After Hunter's
death, the 13,600 specimens which the
museum eventually contained were offered
by his executors for sale to the Government.
Pitt, then Prime Minister, was reputed to
have said :

'What ! Buy preparations. Why, I have not
money enough to purchase gunpowder.'
(1799).

Eventually, however, the Government did
buy the collection, paying £15,000 for it, a
little more than one pound per specimen. In
view of all this, it is rather sad to have to
record that the famous collection, which was
almost lost to the British nation because of

15 *Alleged effects of vaccination*

gunpowder, was eventually partly destroyed by the effects of the latter's modern equivalent when the buildings of the Royal College of Surgeons of England, where it was housed, suffered so heavily from enemy action almost a century and a half later.

Edward Jenner and vaccination

John Hunter had many pupils who achieved fame, but one of them, a country practitioner Edward Jenner (1749–1823), was destined to have a most profound effect on medical thought and practice and became one of the greatest benefactors of humanity.

In the eighteenth century, smallpox was a prevalent disease with a high mortality and the capacity to mark and disfigure those whom it did not kill. The idea of vaccination was put into Jenner's mind by hearing a dairymaid[1] remark :

'I can't take smallpox for I have already had cowpox.'

He found that it had been well known in Gloucestershire for a long time that milkers who contracted the mild cowpox from the udders of cows did not develop smallpox. In 1796 he vaccinated his first case with cowpox and, in a manner which his teacher, John Hunter, would have highly approved, completed the experiment by innoculating the patient with smallpox virus ! No smallpox developed ; the experiment was successful ; Jenner was famous and a new weapon of great power had been given

[1] Her name was Sarah Nelmes. She may well be the most famous dairymaid in history.

47

&c.

This Day is published, Price One Shilling,

A LETTER

FROM

JOHN BIRCH, Esq.

TO THE

EDITOR of the " Fatal Effects of Cow Pox
AT RINGWOOD, MISSENDEN, AND OTHER PLACES."

In this Publication are noticed,

The Parliamentary Grant of £30,000 to Dr. JENNER, for an
unsuccessful Experiment ;

A Letter, proving the Production of a new and fatal
Appearance, called, the

VACCINE ULCER,

Described by ASTLEY COOPER, *Esq. Surgeon of Guy's
Hospital, &c.*

A Letter from Mr. WESTCOTT, of *Ringwood,* proving the
Failures of the Experiment at that Place ;

A List of those who died of Cow-pox there ;

A List of those who were defectively vaccinated, and took
Small-pox afterward ; and of those who died of Small-pox,
after having been vaccinated, and assured of Protection !

A List of some Failures under the Treatment of the
Vice President of the Jennerian Institution ;

AND SEVERAL RECENT CASES.

To which is added,

AN APPENDIX.

INCLUDING THE

Accusations of the Vaccine Societies against each other; and
shewing the Fallacy, Prevarication, and Subtilty of the
RINGWOOD Report from Salisbury Court, published under
the Authority of Dr. JENNER.

Qui facit per alium, facit per se ?

Published by J. F. HUGHES, 15, Paternoster Row, and 5, Wigmore
Street, Cavendish Square; and W. BRUCE, 10, New Round Court,
Strand, London.——Sold also by Gibbons, Bath; Street, South-
ampton; Webb, Bedford; Mackie, Edinburgh; Morrison, York;
Bristow & Cowten, Canterbury; at the Herald Office, Glouces-
ter; by Jenkins, Swansea; Pearson, Holyhead; La Grange & Co.
Dublin; and Connor, Corke.

NEIL, Printer, 448, (Corner of New Round Court) STRAND.

16 *All new discoveries have their detractors*

17 *The Battle of the Barbers and Surgeons*

to medicine.

Before the close of the year 1800, many thousands of people had been vaccinated. Present-day methods of immunisation follow directly from Jenner's successful introduction of vaccination. It is interesting to think what the world owes to the chance remark of a dairymaid and a man who had an idea and the courage and strength of mind to develop it.

Surgery in France

Apart from in France, the status of surgeons was generally very low during most of the eighteenth century. The social status of French surgeons was raised when Louis XIV fortunately made a successful recovery from a rectal operation. In 1724, not without some opposition from physicians, five chairs of surgical instruction were created. In 1731 the Academy of Surgery was founded and finally in 1743 Louis XV delivered the surgeons from their then outmoded and unnecessary association with barbers and wig-makers.[1] After this no one could become a Master of Surgery unless he was first a Master of Arts. Because of these enlightened measures, Paris became an important surgical centre for most of the eighteenth century. Its status rapidly declined after the Revolution of 1789. In London surgeons were separated from the barbers in 1745 and the Surgeons' Company was formed. From this developed the present Royal College of Surgeons of England.

Medicine in America

The War of the Revolution (1775–83) provided the stimulus to American medicine

[1] In Edinburgh, surgeons were legally separated from barbers in 1722.

that had been lacking until that time. Washington's two Surgeons-General, Morgan and Shippen, did a great deal for American medical education and also played a prominent part in organising medical services during the war. Both these men were Edinburgh graduates and both had also studied under the Hunters. Intolerance and jealousy caused the dismissal of one and the other was court-martialled in 1780. Both were eventually vindicated. Shippen was the second of seven generations of American doctors bearing that name. Generally speaking American doctors of the late 1700s and the early 1800s were importers of ideas, seldom exporters, and they looked to Europe for leadership and advice. However, important exceptions gradually developed and we will hear about them later.

Captain Cook's surgeons

An observant passer-by on the wharves of the busy English port of Plymouth in August 1768 might have noted two young men superintending the loading of certain stores onto the bark *Endeavour*. This vessel was under the command of Captain James Cook, and the two young men were his surgeons, William Monkhouse and William Perry.

50

They were particularly concerned with the loading and storage of casks containing lemon juice and also other medical stores. Both were keen and conscientious young men and both had surely read James Lind's[1] classic work, which had been written in 1753. Lind was a naval surgeon who had been entrusted with the care of, on occasions, more than three hundred cases of scurvy in the wards of Haslar Hospital. Lind did not know anything about vitamins, but advocated the use of lemon and lime juices and fresh vegetables in the treatment of scurvy.

Monkhouse and Perry followed his principles and proved the truth of what he had written. In the long voyage which lasted nearly three years, only one man died of scurvy, which was remarkable for those days. Anson, in his voyage around the world some thirty years earlier, had lost seventy-five per cent of his ship's company from the same cause. After discovering and exploring the east coast of Australia, Captain Cook brought the *Endeavour* through Torres Strait to Batavia (now Indonesia). Here Monkhouse died of some serious epidemic

[1] James Lind (1716–1794), founder of naval hygiene in England, wrote on scurvy, tropical medicine and naval hygiene. He was a pupil of that remarkable man Hermann Boerhaave.

which was raging on the island. Cook wrote in his diary :

'Mr Monkhouse, our surgeon, a skilful sensible man, fell the first sacrifice to this fatal country, a loss which was greatly aggravated by our situation.'

Medicine and the Industrial Revolution in England

During the eighteenth century, because of drastic changes in industry brought about by the use of mechanical power, towns increased rapidly in number and very rapidly in size. This movement, which started first in England, sooner or later influenced all civilised countries. Gaining in impetus and strength as the century progressed, it became completely out of hand in the nineteenth century.

London's problems
In 1800 London was the only city in the British Isles with a population greater than 100,000. By 1841 its population had increased by over a million and that of Manchester had quadrupled. This type of explosive increase applied to all manufacturing towns. As people flocked to these centres some sort of accommodation had to be found for them. As wages were extremely low and as the rent of a house was dependent on its capital cost, the type of accommodation provided for a family can well be imagined : or can it be imagined ?

Let us look back and try to form a picture of London between 1780 and 1820. The main streets of the city were fine thoroughfares containing many imposing buildings. The attractive shops with their small window-panes contained much that was beautiful—furniture designed by Chippendale and Sheraton, silver in the Adam or Regency style and porcelain from Derby or Worcester. It was indeed an age of elegance in the proud city of London.

However, away from the main streets things could be very different. Anyone walking north from the Strand into that area extending from Lincoln's Inn Fields to where Regent Street now is, would enter one huge incredible stinking slum. In many parts of this area no water was available and most of the inhabitants were forced to buy what they needed for one halfpenny per pail. Most of the water available was pumped from the Thames into which nearly all of London's sewers drained ! Sanitary arrangements were almost non-existent and the disposal of sewage primitive in the extreme. In some of the worst areas refuse, excreta and filth were simply thrown into the lanes or courts surrounding the houses. Any water-course acted as an open sewer, the most infamous of these being the river Fleet which had been associated with smells and filth for centuries.

A similar state of affairs could be found in Bethnal Green, Bermondsey and Lambeth, and matters were even worse in many provincial cities and towns. As populations grew, overcrowding everywhere became more and more of a problem, and by 1840 conditions were such that not more than one workman in six had more than a single room for himself, his wife and his children. Often three or four families had but one room to live in.

Improvements in hygiene in the towns of England started about the middle of the eighteenth century and continued through most of the next. In favour of reform was the natural kindliness and decency of a large body of people, most of whom became disgusted by the revolting way in which human beings were forced to live. Despite this, many of the more privileged people were able to put up with the sufferings which went on around them with much the same degree of fortitude that so many of us exhibit today in the face of similar but less obvious problems.

It must be admitted that the force which produced the most sweeping changes was fear, and once the public discovered that it was endangered by the existing insanitary conditions, improvement fairly rapidly followed.

Cholera epidemics occurred in England on four occasions between 1831 and 1866, and each one of these epidemics was followed by improvements in sanitation. At first these were carried out under the ancient handicap of the 'miasma' theory, and no real scientific advances were made until Pasteur's work and the development of the germ theory in the 'sixties and 'seventies. By 1870 London's sewage system was properly established but its water supply was not put on an organised basis until 1899.

Gaol Fever and John Howard
During these times, gaols were pestilential dens where the unfortunate prisoners lived in filth and often died of what was called gaol fever. The judges who sentenced them to death or transportation did so (still thinking in terms of the miasma) over a large bunch of fragrant flowers, not knowing that the danger lay not in the smell given off by the unhappy prisoners but in the lice which lived in their filthy clothes and bodies.

These insects carried the organisms of

typhus fever, but this was not discovered until 1916.[1]

However, the fact that typhus fever was associated with dirt and starvation was recognised by some observers. John Howard (1726–90), at great personal risk and in the face of the usual opposition, conducted a tour of the gaols of England and Wales. He advocated medical attention for prisoners, the segregation of the sick, and simple methods of hygiene and cleanliness, which included baths, soap and water, and fumigation of the clothes. As a result of this campaign typhus fever slowly but surely diminished.

Although the lessons taught by Howard made a successful impression, it is sad to have to record that these lessons were quite rapidly forgotten.

In 1812 James Neild found that he had to fight Howard's battles again and he did this with courage and success. Elizabeth Fry (1780–1845) did a great deal to improve the conditions of female prisoners in Newgate. She was the remarkable product of a Quaker family and we will hear of her again.

[1] The organism responsible for typhus was discovered by da Rocha Lima in 1916. Earlier work had been done, by Howard T. Rickotts who died in Mexico City in 1910 of typhus fever, a victim of the disease he was studying.

7 Medicine in the nineteenth century

The task of the medical historian becomes more complicated with the approach of modern times. Some of us can reach back into the nineteenth century through our grandparents' memories and because of that this most important period does not seem so very far away. All that can be done in this brief survey of medical history is to consider the work of a few of the many distinguished medical men of the times and to discuss some of the more important trends of thought and practice.

It is wise to remember that, almost without exception, no single advance, however spectacular, has ever been completely dependent on the activities and thoughts of any one man. Someone has gone before, a teacher perhaps, another investigator maybe, who has left behind him some indication of the way to go. This is particularly true at the present time when research is so often carried out by teams of investigators and scientists rather than by any one person.

Charles Bell

At the turn of the century a young Scot by name Charles Bell (1774–1842) was beginning to make a name for himself in London. In 1812 he acquired the famous

Windmill Street School of Anatomy which had been commenced by the Hunters. There he taught and dissected and there he carried out research on the functions of nerves. He eventually made the great discovery that there were two kinds of nerves, the one conveying sensation to the brain and the other the impulses which pass outwards from the brain and which cause muscles to contract.[1] These two types of nerves became known as sensory and motor nerves respectively.

Bell was a very good artist and he wrote and beautifully illustrated the first textbook on neurology. Medical students will always remember him because a nerve on the side of the wall of the chest bears his name, as also does a type of temporary paralysis involving the muscles on one side of the face. He was knighted in 1831 and his standing both at home and abroad was immense. When he visited Paris Professor Roux dismissed his class with these words:

> 'C'est assez, Messieurs, vous avez vu Charles Bell!'[2]

[1] For a century there has been controversy as to whether Bell or François Magendie of Bordeaux was the real discoverer of the spinal nerve-roots. There is a case for stating that Magendie made the crucial experiments, but whether he initiated the research or confirmed Bell's work still seems uncertain.

[2] Guthrie, Douglas, *A History of Medicine*, 1945, p 269.

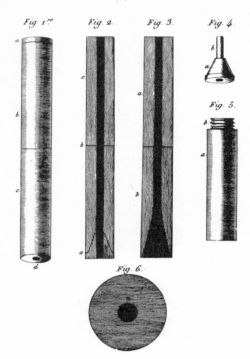

Fig. 1ᵉʳ Fig. 2. Fig. 3. Fig. 4.

Fig. 5.

18 *The first stethoscope*

Fig. 6.

through the instrument, but also identified and discussed the underlying lung disease and chest pathology that caused them. He died in 1826 of pulmonary tuberculosis, a victim of a disease which he had done so much to study and clarify.

Kipling[1] describes Laënnec's first attempts at making stethoscopes and mentions some of the difficulties he encountered.

While we are in France let us see what is happening there during these times. With the wealth of material that is available, only a few outstanding figures can be mentioned.

The inventor of the stethoscope

René Laënnec (1781–1826) was appointed a physician to the Necker Hospital in Paris in 1816. He was the inventor of the stethoscope which since then has gradually come to be regarded as a kind of medical badge of office. The first stethoscopes were made of wood, bell-shaped at one end and about a foot long. Hospital legends report that many nineteenth century physicians carried these stethoscopes in their top hats ! Laënnec, in a famous book, not only described and named the various lung sounds heard

Baron Larrey, surgeon of Napoleon

The light in the tent was not very good, but Dominique Jean Larrey (1766–1842) knew very well who was seated at the small portable desk. He knew why his Emperor had sent for him and he also knew who had complained against him.

'And is it true', said an icy voice, 'that you have dared to kill my officers' horses to feed your wounded ?' 'Yes, sire', answered Larrey.

'Well', said Napoleon with a dramatic pause, 'I will make you a Baron of the Empire'. This he did.

The honour was well deserved because Baron Larrey was probably the greatest military surgeon since Ambroise Paré. Like

[1] Kipling, Rudyard, *Rewards and Fairies—Marklake Witches*, p 89.

19 *Claude Bernard,*
the father of experimental medicine

Paré he won the esteem and affection of the troops and like Paré he never spared himself in their service. Quite early in his career he introduced light, well-sprung, horse-drawn ambulances which could be rushed up to the front lines, thus allowing soldiers to be collected soon after they had been wounded. In this way he brought hospital services directly to the wounded and in so doing saved many lives.

He won the friendship and esteem of Napoleon who bequeathed him the sum of 100,000 francs.

Claude Bernard

Claude Bernard (1813–78) was a great French physiologist who is generally regarded as being the father of experimental medicine. Probably his greatest achievement was the discovery that the liver had the

power of building up and storing certain complicated substances derived from food and carried to the liver by the blood-stream. The substances thus formed, and particularly the one known as glycogen, can be released at any time to supply the needs of the body.

Bernard also solved the problem associated with the digestion of fats. He showed that the essential process of fat digestion was the splitting up of fats into fatty acids and glycerine by the actions of the secretions of the pancreas gland.

His third great achievement was his discovery that the flow of blood in the arteries themselves is regulated by an elaborately balanced system of nerves of two different kinds.

One set of these nerves has the power to constrict and the other the power to dilate the blood vessels. This is known as the vasomotor mechanism and the importance of this process cannot be overestimated. For example it is this mechanism that allows the brain to be properly supplied with blood, no matter what posture is assumed.

The influence of Claude Bernard's ideas was very great. His mind was of that peculiarly French type to which guess-work and mysticism were abhorrent. Regarding experimental work he laid down the dictates that any investigation which could only do

20 *The Conquest of Rabies. Statue of Jupille,
Pasteur's patient, and the mad dog in the
courtyard of the* Institut Pasteur, *Paris*

harm should be forbidden ; that which was
innocent was permitted and that which
could do good was obligatory. He was a
notable man.

Pasteur and the germ origin of disease

In 1885 a young French shepherd lad from
the Jura, by name Jupille, courageously
went to the assistance of some young
children who were being attacked by a mad
dog. In doing this he risked his life because,
as everybody knew, sufferers from rabies or
hydrophobia, the disease caused by the bite

of a mad dog, always died. It is impossible
to know what Jupille's emotions were when
he realised that, although his brave action
had saved his comrades, he had himself
been bitten in the struggle ! Perhaps he took
comfort from stories that were going about
concerning the wonderful work of a man
who came from his own part of France, from
nearby Dôle. Was it not true that he had
saved the life of another boy, Joseph
Meister from Alsace, who had also been
bitten by a mad dog some months earlier ?

Jupille's faith was not misplaced. He was
taken to Louis Pasteur (1822–95) and he
was saved by that kindly genius who was
endowed with a mind the quality and
intensity of which have been compared to a
blow-pipe flame.

Pasteur knew about Jenner's work and
following the lines laid down by him,
prepared a weak culture[1] of the rabies
organism and inoculated the boy with it.
This was followed by complete immunity.

A statue of Jupille stands in the Pasteur
Institute of Paris. But what of Pasteur
himself ? He was not a medical man, but the
quality of his genius was such that any
profession would have been proud to claim
him. What he did for medicine was of

[1] An old culture or growth of the germ, possessing low
virulence.

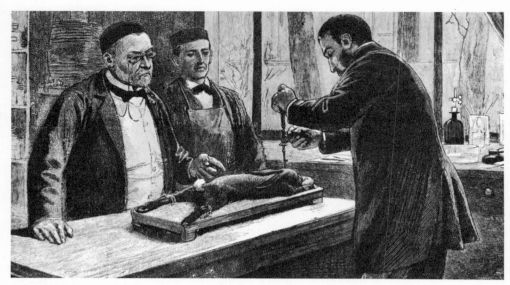

21 *Monsieur Pasteur's experiments for the cure of hydrophobia*

incalculable value. He was trained as a chemist and during his long working life he solved problem after problem. In so doing he conferred inestimable benefits on mankind.

His first researches led him to the momentous discovery that fermentation was not purely a chemical process but that micro-organisms played a vital part in it. Working at Lille he discovered that certain bacilli were the cause of sourness in wine or milk. He discovered that these changes could be controlled by the application of a degree of heat, a process which became known as 'pasteurisation'. His next difficulty was to decide where such organisms came from. Did they arrive by a process of spontaneous generation or were they present in the air? The answer to the question was of vital importance for reasons that will soon be given.

Critics who opposed the idea of airborne infection argued with some superiority that if Pasteur's theories were correct, then the

air that everyone breathed must be, so to speak, almost stiff with germs. They thought in terms of spontaneous generation, holding the view that if life must begin somewhere, what better place than a cask of wine or a bottle of milk?

In the end Pasteur settled the matter by an experiment that was completely convincing. Its very simplicity carried the stamp of his genius. He took a flask which had a long tubular S-shaped neck and filled it with a fluid known to be subject to fermentation or decomposition. After any organisms present had been killed by boiling, the flask was left in a still room free from excessive air currents. Air was able to enter the flask, but any floating germs settled on the floor of the long S-shaped neck of the flask.

Under these circumstances Pasteur showed that the fluid would remain sterile for months. If, however, the long curved neck of the flask were broken off, allowing germs to enter freely from the air, fermentation or putrefaction would start within a matter of hours. As we shall learn later, it was Pasteur's proof of the existence of airborne germs that led Lister to apply the same knowledge to surgery with such success that ever since surgery has been referred to as pre- or post-Listerian !

Other work done by this remarkable man included research into diseases of silkworms, micro-organisms in beer, the study of anthrax and chicken cholera, and vaccination against certain diseases (especially hydrophobia). By his activities and genius he saved the silk industry for France and also prevented devastating losses from disease in cattle, sheep and fowl.

He was elected to the French Academy of Medicine, which was a very unusual honour for a non-medical man. On his seventieth birthday an historic meeting took place in Paris. Pasteur, leaning on the arm of the President of France, for the first time met Lister, who said of him :

'Truly there does not exist in the wide world an individual to whom medical science owes more than you.'

In answering him Pasteur said :

'Science and peace must triumph over ignorance and war. Nations will unite not to destroy but to instruct one another and that the future will belong to those who have

22 *Robert Koch, Nobel Laureate, 1905*

done most for suffering humanity. I refer to you, my dear Lister . . . .'

Then Pasteur and Lister embraced amid cheers and shouts of '*Vive Pasteur*'.

Successors to Pasteur

In France Pasteur was succeeded by his assistant Émile Roux, and in Germany by Robert Koch and Emil von Behring. Together with Pasteur these men must be regarded as being the founders of bacteriology.

Roux (1853–1933) perfected the development of anti-diphtheric serum and made other important discoveries. He followed Pasteur as director of the Pasteur Institute.

Robert Koch (1843–1910) carried out important research on the life history of the anthrax bacillus which had been discovered by Davaine in 1850. He was the first to evolve the method of growing organisms in the laboratory on gelatinous surfaces. This allowed each kind of germ to grow in a separate colony on this solid surface, making the study of its characteristics much easier. In 1882 he announced the discovery of the germ which causes tuberculosis and that particular germ is still called Koch's bacillus. A year later he discovered the vibrio or virus of cholera and showed how it was transmitted by infected drinking water.

Koch travelled extensively, visiting Africa to study rinderpest[1] and India to look for the cause of plague. He also went to Java where he studied malaria. He received many honours, including a Nobel Prize which he won in 1905. Germany has produced a great number of scientists, but none greater than Robert Koch whose productive life was of such benefit to humanity

Emil von Behring (1854–1917) discovered the principle of serum treatment and is the founder of the science of immunology. He worked for some time with a Japanese pupil of Koch's, by name Shibasaburo Kitasato (1852–1931). This man discovered in 1894 the bacillus which causes plague and founded and became first Director of the Japanese Institute for Infectious Disease.

In Britain the new science of bacteriology was developed by, along with many others, Sir Almroth Wright (1861–1947), who was a pioneer of vaccine treatment.

In America, Theobald Smith (1859–1934) and William Welch (1850–1934) gained distinction. Welch, who discovered the germ which causes gas gangrene, a virulent form of wound infection, was a colleague of William Osler (see p 84) at Johns Hopkins University.

Puerperal fever

There is no doubt that, in the case of several diseases, the method of the spread of infection and means of prevention have been appreciated a long time before bacteria were actually demonstrated. A conspicuous example of this was the case of the dreaded puerperal fever, an often fatal infection of women who had recently borne children.

In 1773 Charles White of Manchester stressed the necessity of strict cleanliness and adequate ventilation of the birth-room, and in 1795 Alexander Gordon of Aberdeen advised doctors and nurses who had

[1] German for 'cattle-plague' : a fatal, contagious disease affecting oxen and transmissible to other ruminants.

23 *Dr Oliver Wendell Holmes,*
who invented the name anaesthesia

attended women with the disease to wash themselves and to fumigate their clothing before attending another case.

In 1843 Oliver Wendell Holmes (1809–94) read a medical paper in Boston entitled *On the Contagiousness of Puerperal Fever*, in which he maintained that women in childbirth should not be attended by a physician who was treating another patient with puerperal infection or who had recently conducted a post-mortem examination. Again thorough washings and changes of clothing were recommended.

The degree of antagonism aroused among his American colleagues by these suggestions was unbelievable. It must be remembered that this sort of thing has always happened to great reformers, no matter where they are. Pettiness, professional jealousy, greed, personal dislike, are factors which although undesirable can at least be understood. More subtle but probably far more potent were the unbearable feelings of guilt that such suggestions conjured up. Just think of it !

'Because I was not careful, because I was not clean, I have caused the deaths of some, perhaps many, women.'

Such an idea would be intolerable to most people, and it is not hard to understand how it would be quickly replaced by resentment and aggression.

The triumph and the tragedy of Semmelweiss
Four years after Holmes' controversial paper was read, a doctor in the Maternity Hospital in Vienna, by name Ignaz Phillip Semmelweiss (1818–65) made his great contribution.

An obstetrician, he was greatly disturbed by the high mortality from puerperal fever, but like all his associates he was unable to understand it or lessen it. Eventually a friend, Professor Kolletscka, received a wound during a post-mortem examination and died of blood-poisoning. At his autopsy Semmelweiss noted the resemblance between the changes in his tissues and those seen in the organs of women dying of puerperal fever. The realisation that his friend's death had resulted from contamination of the wound by some poisonous material from the cadaver provided a possible explanation for another important and worrying problem. There were two obstetric clinics in the *Allgemeines*

61

Krankenhaus at Vienna. In one, the patients were delivered by students, and the mortality was very high ; in the other midwives delivered the patients, and the mortality was quite low. Semmelweiss showed that students (but not the midwives) attended classes of pathological anatomy and post-mortem examinations. They then examined their obstetric patients, thus introducing the infection from their hands and clothes. As Semmelweiss wrote in 1847, 'Puerperal fever is caused by conveyance to the pregnant woman of putrid particles derived from living organisms'.

After the institution of the simple expedient of washing the hands in calcium chloride solution before entering the wards and between examinations, the mortality rate tumbled within two years from 18 per cent to a little over 1 per cent. Thus Semmelweiss became the pioneer of antisepsis in midwifery and the first person to recognise puerperal fever for what it really is, that is a form of blood-poisoning. Like Holmes, he met with fierce opposition, and the persecution he endured caused him to leave Vienna and go to Budapest where he became in due course Professor of Obstetrics at the University.

About three weeks before his death in 1865, he became insane quite suddenly.

The cause of his death was ascending infection from a wound on a finger of his right hand. It is generally believed that this occurred during one of his last operations.

Semmelweiss [1,2] was one of medicine's great but tragic figures. Born before his time, he lacked the inspiration and help of a Pasteur, and therefore had no knowledge of the germ origin of infective processes. The worth of his work is beyond dispute. Lister acknowledged his genius, and every child-bearing woman owes him a debt of gratitude. He was mostly alone in his uphill fight, but as Steinbeck[3] has said : 'Nothing of importance was ever created by two men. Once the miracle of creation has taken place, the group can build and extend it ; but the group never invents anything. The preciousness lies in the lonely mind of man.'

Conquerors of pain

Always accompanying the surgeon was the knowledge that all surgical operations were associated with dreadful pain which he was

[1] Sinclair, W. S., *Semmelweiss: His Life and his Doctrine*, University Press, Manchester (1909).
[2] Thompson, Morton, *The Cry and the Covenant*, Heinemann (London).
[3] Steinbeck, John, *East of Eden*, Heinemann (London).

powerless to prevent. Only by speed and dexterity could the ordeal be shortened but even in the best hands a three-minute operation must have seemed like a lifetime. Under those circumstances it now seems extraordinary that when Sir Humphrey Davy (1778–1829)[1] wrote in 1799 that nitrous oxide (or laughing gas, as it came to be called), when inhaled, was capable of abolishing pain and might with advantage be used in surgical operations, the idea was not followed up.

In 1815 his assistant, Michael Faraday (1791–1867)[2] noted that the inhalation of ether had a similar effect. This profound observation also passed unnoticed and for another thirty years or so mankind was forced to suffer surgical agony, although methods of relief were available.

It seems that nature's secrets are only fully revealed to man when his mind and vision develop sufficiently to accept new ideas.[3]

The practical use of effective anaesthesia

dated from 1842, when Dr Crawford W. Long (1815–78) used ether in his practice in Jefferson, Georgia. However, because of the worries of a large general practice, coupled perhaps with some lack of enterprise, he did not publish any report of his discovery until 1849.

In 1844 Horace Wells (1815–1848), a dentist of Hartford, Connecticut, sought and secured permission to give a demonstration of painless tooth extraction at the Harvard Medical School. He endeavoured to administer nitrous oxide but failed to give enough. This was not surprising because the art of anaesthesia requires training and experience, and nitrous oxide by itself is not an easy anaesthetic agent to employ. At any rate the demonstration ended in failure, discrediting both Wells and nitrous oxide.

A man who had helped to arrange this demonstration and who almost certainly attended it was a former partner of Wells, called William Thomas Green Morton (1819–68). As he also had found difficulties in the administration of nitrous oxide, on the advice of a Dr Charles Jackson (who had possibly read of Faraday's observations) he tried ether.

On October 16th 1846 a successful operation was carried out painlessly under ether anaesthesia at the Massachusetts

[1] A famous chemist, inventor of the miner's safety lamp, and President of the Royal Society.
[2] Chemist and natural philosopher, famous for his researches on electricity and electromagnetism.
[3] 'It is hardly too much to say that no major discovery destined to be fully incorporated into established knowledge and techniques is made more than a year or two before it is inevitable.'
Burnett, Sir F. M., *Medical Journal of Australia*, Vol. 1, *Listerian Oration*, 1952, p 801.

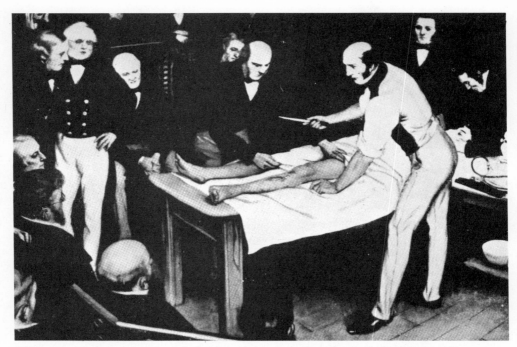

24 *The first use of ether anaesthesia in Britain at University College Hospital in 1846. Robert Liston performs an amputation. Young Lister (seen at left in profile) stands facing Liston*

General Hospital. At the termination of the operation the surgeon, John Collins Warren (1778–1856), made a remark that has since become famous and was probably one of the great understatements of all time. He said :

'Gentlemen, this is no humbug.'

Because of Warren's status as a man and as a surgeon, ether anaesthesia was given a most helpful introduction to surgery. The medical profession was quick to grasp and use the new discovery, and the first operation in the Old World under ether anaesthesia was carried out by Dr Robert Liston (1794–1847)[1] at University College

Hospital, London, on December 21st 1846. Among those who witnessed the operation was a young student, Joseph Lister by name.

A great controversy soon arose in America, the claims of Long, Wells, Morton and Jackson all being advocated by their various supporters. All these people were contestants for a prize of one hundred thousand dollars offered by the United States Congress to the discoverer of anaesthesia. Because the claimants and their representatives could not agree, the argument went on for years and the award was never made ! It is easy to say now that there should have been enough glory and money to satisfy four people. Easy enough, until one remembers the many wars that have occurred since then and the millions who

[1] An Edinburgh graduate who became a famous and dexterous surgeon at the Royal Infirmary. In 1835 he was appointed to the Chair of Surgery at University College Hospital, London.

have died, because mankind finds it hard to agree.

In 1847 Dr James Young Simpson (1811–70), who was Professor of midwifery in Edinburgh, began experimenting with various gaseous substances, searching for a replacement for ether which he considered too irritating for midwifery patients. One evening he and some friends inhaled a drug which had been discovered in 1831 and which was called chloroform. When Simpson finally regained consciousness after a decidedly hazardous journey into the unknown and found his colleagues still lying unconscious about him, he realised that he had discovered a new and potent anaesthetic agent.

In many quarters there was strong opposition to the use of chloroform. This was partly due to some deaths which occurred because of lack of knowledge of the drug's powerful properties and partly due to a natural opposition towards anything new. Simpson was also forced to defend chloroform against critics who attacked it on moral grounds, supporting their arguments by selected Biblical quotations. However, Simpson fought back vigorously, finding suitable counter-quotations from the Bible. He reminded his opponents that, before the creation of Eve,

'The Lord God caused a deep sleep to fall on Adam.'

He also pointed out that the verse,

'In sorrow thou shalt bring forth children', does not mean 'in pain thou shalt bring forth children'.

When Queen Victoria accepted chloroform anaesthesia during the birth of her eighth child, the controversy rapidly subsided.

To Davy, Faraday, Long, Wells, Morton, Jackson and Simpson the world owes a great debt of gratitude. Oliver Wendell Holmes, who invented the name anaesthesia, wrote of the discoverers as follows:

'By this priceless gift to humanity, the fierce extremity of suffering has been steeped in the waters of forgetfullness and the deepest furrow in the knotted brow of agony has been smoothed forever.'

The battle against infection; and progress in surgery

Lister and his work

Although anaesthetics were quickly and generally adopted and the number of operations performed by surgeons increased greatly, yet the mortality associated with such procedures was not materially reduced. In fact the death rate in hospitals was appalling. Wounds caused by the surgeon's knife refused to heal and the spectres of gangrene

65

and infection haunted all hospitals. Patients went in deadly fear and the surgeons themselves lived in constant anxiety and frustration. This was the state of affairs a little more than one hundred years ago.

Let us go back in time to this period and let us imagine that we have the power to look into one of the long surgical wards in the Glasgow Royal Infirmary. We see a man sitting at a desk and he is thinking deeply. He is a surgeon and the ward is filled with his patients, many of whom are fighting for their lives. There they lie, tossing in pain and high fever, victims of a seemingly inevitable and frequently fatal septic infection.

Surely he, Joseph Lister, had done everything possible for his patients ? Then why do these dreadful things happen ? Surely wound infection and sepsis must be due to some sort of putrefaction which, because it is universal and spreads so quickly, can only come from something in the air ? He asks himself as he had asked a hundred times before, 'what is that something ?'

Let us imagine that the very day on which we are watching is the momentous day when a letter and a parcel arrive for Joseph Lister. The letter is from his friend Thomas Anderson, Professor of Chemistry, and it draws his attention to the published findings of a young French chemist, one Louis Pasteur. We can see his expression change as he scans the article and realises that Pasteur claims to have demonstrated conclusively that fermentation and putrefaction are brought about by the actions of micro-organisms or bacteria. Although the smell of decaying flesh still fills his nostrils and the groans of the sick and dying his ears, a look of hope can be seen dawning on his face. Could it be that this was the answer that he had been looking for ? Could it be that ?

Here we must leave the realms of fantasy and return to historical facts.

Joseph Lister (1827–1912) was born at Upton, Essex. He was the last and greatest of a famous line of English doctors who were Quakers, and he inherited, along with his beliefs, the simplicity, kindness and control so often met with amongst the Society of Friends. Lister entered University College Hospital as a student. He graduated in 1852 and later became a Fellow of the Royal College of Surgeons of England. He studied under Liston and later went to Edinburgh where he continued his surgical education under James Syme (1799–1870)[1].

---

[1] Professor of Clinical Surgery at the University of Edinburgh, a brilliant surgeon with a European reputation. It has been said of him that 'he never wasted a word, a drop of ink or a drop of blood'.

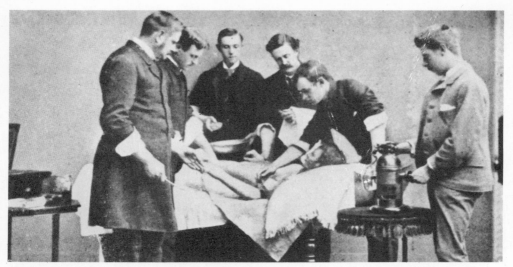

25 *An operation in Lister's time. An assistant attends to the carbolic spray as used by Lister. The era of gowns, caps, masks and gloves had not dawned*

In 1856 he married Syme's eldest daughter, Agnes. The marriage was a very happy one and for the next thirty-nine years she devoted her life to his work.

In 1860 Lister was appointed Professor of Clinical Surgery in the University of Glasgow, and it was there that his greatest contributions to medicine were made. When he learnt from Pasteur that wound infection was to all intents a fermentation due to the growth of minute living organisms carried by the air, the course which must be followed became clear to him. The problem was to exclude these minute forms of life from wounds, during and after surgery.

The first solution, or perhaps partial solution, was found in what was known as 'Antiseptic Surgery'.[1] Lister realised that he must deal with germs present on the patients'

skin and also on his own hands and instruments. To solve these problems he evolved a spray pump which produced a fine mist of carbolic acid, and in this antiseptic atmosphere he conducted his operations.

The first trial of this new system took place in March 1865 in a case of open or compound fracture of the leg. The usual outcome of such an injury was the tragic sequence of wound infection, bone inflammation, blood-poisoning and death. This case, however, was outstandingly different because none of these things happened. It was the first of a series of eleven cases described by Lister in 1867.

He published, in a medical journal, a description of his methods and results: eleven cases, nine of whom recovered with intact limbs, one amputation and one death. Many criticisms were heaped on this paper, but most of them were directed towards unimportant details of method and procedure and not towards the underlying

[1] Antisepsis means countering and controlling the process of infection, while asepsis means the use of cleanliness in preventing it from ever starting. The present aseptic method of surgery developed gradually from the antiseptic teachings of Lister.

principles, which at first many of his critics failed to grasp. Lister was forced to contend with opposition during most of his life. Much of this was hurtful and bitter, but according to one of his famous pupils, Sir St Clair Thompson,

'Lister exhibited no resentment, never retaliated, and only showed how he felt it by the little gasping sigh we all learned to know and respect as his only sign of sorrow or annoyance.'[1]

In 1869 Syme was forced by illness to resign from the Chair of Clinical Surgery at Edinburgh. He was succeeded by his son-in-law, and it was in that city that Lister reached the zenith of his achievements. His clinic attracted visitors from all important medical centres.

In 1875 he visited Germany and in the following year America. Both these countries were eager to adopt new ideas, and he was warmly welcomed and honoured wherever he went.

The third stage of Lister's life started in 1877. In that year Sir William Fergusson (1808–77)[2] died and Lister was invited to

26 *Lord Lister: 'His work will last for all time; humanity will bless him evermore and his fame will be immortal'*

succeed him at King's College. Before he went to London, Lister was aware that his antiseptic doctrines had made little progress in that city. He was not prepared, however, for the apathy and hostility with which he was received and he found that the same battles had to be fought over again.

He lived long enough to see his ideas adopted everywhere and when he died in 1912 the world rose up and called.him blessed. Of all the praise that was then heaped upon him, probably none would have pleased him more than the eulogy of the Royal College of Surgeons of England. It was as follows :

'His gentle nature, imperturbable temper, resolute will, indifference to ridicule and tolerance to hostile criticism, combined to make him one of the noblest of men. His work will last for all time ; humanity will bless him evermore and his fame will be immortal.'

Garrison, Fielding H., *An Introduction to the History of Medicine*, 1929, p 592.

[2] An Edinburgh graduate and pupil of James Syme. He was appointed Professor of Surgery at King's College Hospital at the age of thirty-two. He became the most eminent surgeon in London.

After Lister

It is customary in this modern age to refer to surgery as pre-Listerian and post-Listerian. As a result of Lister's work new operative methods were rapidly explored and developed. It is impossible to say with certainty who was the father of abdominal surgery, but perhaps that honour might be given to a German surgeon, Theodore Billroth (1829–94). He taught in Berlin, Zürich and Vienna and was the first to excise a cancerous growth from the stomach.

Another German follower of Lister's was Ernst von Bergmann (1836–1907) of Berlin. He introduced steam sterilisation of instruments and thus played an important part in the development of modern aseptic surgery.

In Switzerland, in his clinic in Berne, Theodore Kocher (1841–1917) as well as being a great surgeon specialised in diseases of the thyroid gland. He performed over 2,000 operations for goitre with a mortality rate of 5 per cent. This was, of course, a remarkable achievement.

Disciples of Lister in America

William Stewart Halstead (1852–1922) was a follower of Lister. He was Professor of Surgery in the Johns Hopkins University, Baltimore. He did much experimental work in surgery, especially in factors governing the healing of wounds. Perhaps his greatest claim to fame was that he was the first to introduce rubber gloves to the operating theatre, which was a great surgical advance.

Rubber gloves are now universally used by surgeons during operations. If a glove becomes punctured during an operation it is immediately changed. It has been shown that the human hand, because of its capacity to sweat, cannot be kept sterile for long. Therefore gloves, which can be easily sterilised, played a significant part in the prevention of wound infection.

The Mayo Brothers

In 1865, in a small cottage in Rochester, Minnesota, a son was born to Dr and Mrs William Mayo. This cottage was situated almost exactly on the spot where, more than fifty years later, a fountain bubbled in the entrance hall of a building which had become a great surgical centre not only for the United States but also for all the world. The new son was named Charles and he had a brother who was four years older, named William. These two brothers rose to surgical fame almost as one man and between them they established the famous Mayo Clinic. Both of these men, who were intensely hard-working, set themselves the highest

28 *The Mayo Clinic buildings*

27 *William James Mayo: 'We were given the opportunity. We were born at the right time and to the right parents'*

standard in surgery and in teaching. They followed in that stimulating wave of advance that came after Lister and were quick to seize on the advantages of antisepsis and anaesthesia. They exemplified to the fullest degree that extraordinary combination of imagination, intelligence, industry and fortitude that has been exhibited in so many successful American enterprises. As Dr William Mayo is reported to have said[1] :

'Yes, we have accomplished much, my brother and I. But we should have done great things, we were given the opportunity. We were born at the right time and to the

[1] Clapesattle, Helen, *The Doctors Mayo*, University of Minnesota (1941).

right parents. Perhaps no one will ever again have the opportunity to accomplish as much.'

This partnership, which for forty years exercised such a profound influence on American and world medicine, ended in 1939 when both brothers died.

The famous Clinic still remains a monument to their memory, and is still a Mecca in the medical world.

Stimulated by men such as Marion Sims,[1] Halstead, the Mayo Brothers, J. B. Murphy[2] and a host of others, American surgery has advanced rapidly, and in the twentieth century surgical advances in America have been more numerous and important than anywhere else.

Appendicitis
The first person to give the name 'appendicitis' to inflammation of the apparently unnecessary worm-like structure that lies at the junction of the small and large bowels was Reginald Heber Fitz (1843–1913) of Boston. He drew attention to the disease and stressed its relationship to peritonitis.

This was a great advance because neglected appendicitis was, and still is, a killer. The operative removal of the inflamed appendix became almost a popular operation after Sir Frederick Treves (1853–1923) had successfully operated on King Edward VII for appendicitis in 1902. It is interesting to note that Treves performed his first appendix operation in 1887 and that by 1895 the Mayo brothers had operated twelve times for appendicitis.

An American surgeon, Charles McBurney (1845–1913), evolved the so-called 'grid-iron' or muscle-splitting incision that is still almost universally used in the operative removal of the appendix. To become a little fanciful, it could be said that McBurney has left his mark on more people than anyone the world has ever known. If you have had your appendix surgically removed, almost certainly you bear his sign. However, a little reflection will show that you are really much more important than that. As well as McBurney's mark, you carry the marks of Lister, Pasteur (who was not a surgeon), Hunter, Paré, de Mondeville and a host of others, including the man in the cave with the flint knife. Although the knowledge of thousands of years is engraved on your

---

[1] Sims, James Marion (1813–83), the founder of gynaecological surgery in America; an original thinker and a gifted surgeon, who acquired not only an American but also a European reputation.
[2] Murphy, John Benjamin (1857–1916), of Chicago, unrivalled as a surgical teacher; a protagonist of early removal of the inflamed appendix and a pioneer in bowel surgery.

abdomen, less than a hundred years ago you would almost certainly have died of peritonitis.

William Osler

The most famous physician in the New World in the nineteenth century was undoubtedly Sir William Osler (1849–1919).

A Canadian by birth, he was Professor of Medicine successively at Montreal (1874), Philadelphia (1884), Baltimore (1889) and Oxford (1904).

He was a magnificent clinical teacher who adorned every appointment that he held and who acquired during his lifetime an international reputation.

This is what has been written about him :[1]

'He was one of Nature's chosen. Good looks, distinction, blithe, benignant manners, a sunbright personality, radiant with kind feelings and goodwill towards his fellow men, an Apollonian poise, swiftness and surety of thought and speech, every gift of the gods was his ; and to these were added careful training, unsurpassed clinical ability, the widest knowledge of his subject, the deepest interest in everything human, and a serene hold upon his fellows that was as a seal set upon them.'

[1] Garrison, Fielding H., *An Introduction to the History of Medicine*, 1929, p 631.

Osler was a prolific writer and his famous textbook, *Principles and Practice of Medicine*, first published in 1892, was the best of its kind in the English language. It was translated into many languages and by 1942 was in its fourteenth edition.

No one was more successful than Osler in bringing together medical men and institutions on both sides of the Atlantic. It is unfortunate that men of his calibre and quality are seen so rarely. The world always needs them, never perhaps more than it does at present.

The revolution in nursing and the first women doctors

It is difficult for anyone who has ever visited a modern hospital to imagine how such an institution could be run without the skilled help and unselfish services of trained nurses. However, it is only comparatively recently that such trained personnel has been available.

During medieval times and in Catholic countries after the Reformation, the care of the sick was the responsibility of religious Sisterhoods. In Protestant countries where no such orders existed, things were very different. The occupation of nursing was a despised one and no social or financial benefits were associated with it.

Institute of Nursing Sisters. This work undoubtedly paved the way for her great successor, Florence Nightingale (1820–1910). The work that this remarkable woman carried out in the Crimea and afterwards in England is well known[1, 2] and will not be described in detail here. She was a woman of strong and resolute will and she had the capacity (among her many capacities) to persuade women of social status and education to accept positions of responsibility.[3]

The control of nursing staffs passed into and stayed in the hands of women, and in 1860 the Nightingale Training School for Nurses at St Thomas' Hospital was opened. Thus, she became the founder of modern nursing.

Elizabeth Blackwell (1821–1910) was the first woman medical graduate. Her degree was conferred on her in New York in 1849.

In Britain, after overcoming considerable opposition, Elizabeth Garrett (1836–1917) obtained a diploma. She became indefatigable in her efforts to assist women to become doctors.

The first important reform took place in Germany. A young Lutheran clergyman, Theodor Fliedner (1800–64), together with his wife, founded a hospital called *Kaiserwerth*, where not only were sick people treated, but also deaconesses were trained in nursing and the care of the sick. This work attracted world-wide interest, and eventually thirty-two deaconess houses were established over Europe, Asia Minor and the United States. Among those who visited *Kaiserwerth* was the Quaker philanthropist, Elizabeth Fry (1780–1845). Already she had followed in the footsteps of that great prison reformer, John Howard, and had done notable work amongst the female prisoners of Newgate. After returning from *Kaiserwerth*, Elizabeth Fry founded the

[1] Calder, J. M., *The Story of Nursing*, Methuen's Outlines, 1963, pp 57–64.
[2] Strachey, Lytton, *Eminent Victorians*, Chatto & Windus, London, 1926, pp 115–74.
[3] Cope, Sir Zachary, *Six Disciples of Florence Nightingale*, Pitman (1961).

The development
and growth of specialisation

Because of the improvement of hospitals and
nursing facilities and of other advances
which have been mentioned, medicine and
surgery expanded very rapidly towards the
end of the nineteenth century. Fields became
so wide and new skills so demanding that
automatically the growth of specialisation
followed. With the development of
and dependence on laboratory tests,
and special instruments of diagnosis and
treatment, what might be described as the
'machine age' of medicine commenced.

The trend in medicine was more gradual
and less obvious than in surgery, but
specialisation nevertheless arrived and
gradually general physicians, exemplified
par excellence by Sir William Osler, became
fewer.

Heart diseases (Cardiology), nervous
diseases (Neurology), diseases of children
(Pediatrics), diseases of the eyes
(Ophthalmology), and mental and
emotional disorders (Psychiatry) were
branches of medicine in which specialisation
rapidly developed. Many famous men were
of course associated with the beginnings of
these various specialities ; it is impossible to
name more than a few.

Cardiology and Sir James Mackenzie
Sir James Mackenzie (1853–1925)[1]
worked as a general practitioner in Burnley,
England, for nearly thirty years. During this
phase of his life, he worked on and wrote
about the subject of cardiac irregularities. In
1902 he perfected a device called a
polygraph, which allowed him to record
simultaneously arterial and venous pulses.
By study of these tracings and by long and
patient observation, he eventually came to
the conclusion that certain heart
irregularities were of little significance,
while others were indications of severe
impairment of the heart's function.

Written in a few lines, this work of half a
lifetime perhaps does not seem much.

Let us imagine that you live in England and
were born in 1894. Just after the turn of the
century you are taken to your doctor because
of some minor ailment. During examination
he notices that the rate of your heart-beat
alters when you take a deep breath. He does
not know what this means, but he is a
conscientious man and he decides that he
cannot afford to take risks with your heart.
All active sports are forbidden, and you are
made into a semi-invalid. Eight years later,
your doctor, still keen and conscientious,

[1] Wilson, R. McNair, *The Great Physician*, the life of Sir
James Mackenzie, 1926.

74

hears that some upstart from Burnley is specialising in London and has a lot to say about heart irregularities. Because he has not got a closed mind, your doctor finds time to go to London where he meets Mackenzie. Eventually a consultation is arranged, and as a result of this you are freed from all restrictions and are able to resume a normal life. This has actually happened to people who are living today.

It has been argued that Sir James Mackenzie, because of other medical interests, was not strictly speaking a specialist. However, as no one can deny that he possessed the most important qualification, which is of course special knowledge, there seems little doubt that his claim to be one of the founders of Cardiology rests on a secure and lasting basis. He was one of the greatest of modern physicians. Like Hippocrates, he conducted his observations, treatment and research at the patient's bedside.

Neurology and Psychiatry
The making of a diagnosis often calls for thinking at a high level of complexity. The most difficult diagnostic problems are probably met with in Neurology (the study of nervous diseases), essentially because the anatomy and physiology of the nervous

system are extremely complicated. The story of the early work that was done on the solution of various neurological problems is a fascinating one.

It is to France that we must turn to study the beginnings of modern neurology. One of the most famous teachers of all time was Jean-Martin Charcot. He created a great neurological clinic at the hospital of the Salpêtrière. This clinic became a neurological Mecca for doctors from all parts of the world. Charcot, who was a splendid teacher and gifted orator, presented his cases in a small theatre complete with footlights. Here, in front of his large audience, he often demonstrated and dramatised certain aspects of a patient's condition such as his gait, speech and muscle weaknesses. As well as possessing ability as an actor, Charcot had a first-class mind and wrote extensively and clearly.

Many of his pupils became famous neurologists, and one man in particular was destined completely to alter and revitalise psychiatry.[1] Indeed, it could be said of his work that the full effects are not yet obvious, and that his influence on the medicine of the future is likely to be profound. The name of this man was Sigmund Freud (1856–1939),

[1] The study and treatment of mental and emotional disorders.

who spent most of his life in Vienna.

In order to understand at least partly why his work is so important, let us consider for a moment the work of a man in a quite different field. His name was Rudolf Virchow (1821–1902), and he was a distinguished German pathologist. His great achievement was the conception of the cell (the unit of structure in the body) as being the centre of pathological changes. Putting it perhaps more simply, he regarded the body as a 'cell state in which every cell is a citizen'. Disease was due to illness or conflicts brought about by external factors, or to 'civil war' inside the body itself. Since Virchow's time, his ideas have been considerably modified, but when first put forward they constituted a great advance. Obviously these ideas produced the conception of disease being only a disorder of organs and cells.

For generations, thinking physicians had realised that upsets in the emotional life of an individual could be associated with illness ; but Virchow's concepts caused a general neglect and lack of interest in the emotional aspects of disease. Just as surgery was divorced from medicine in medieval times, to the detriment of both, so were diseases associated with the psyche (the human soul or spirit or mind) dissociated from the general

76

body of medicine in the last century. This was a retrograde step, and it is possible that humanity has paid and is paying very heavily for these mistakes. Freud believed and taught that there were powerful mental processes, hidden beneath the consciousness, which were capable of causing mental and emotional disturbances often translated into physical symptoms. To discover and eliminate these subconscious factors he evolved his system of psycho-analysis, which was designed to unearth and bring to light the hidden trouble-makers.

As Ross[1] puts it : 'A skeleton in the cupboard is a gruesome and fearful thing, but if we look at it often enough it will become only a bag of old bones'.

Freud has been criticised because of his preoccupation with sexual psychology, and some of his followers have undoubtedly suffered from the effects of the weakened bonds between psychiatry and medicine which have been mentioned. In 1946, Guthrie wrote :[1]

'Today medical psychology is permeating all branches of medicine, and it may prove to be the activating factor of a new era in medical science.'

[1] Ross, T. A., *The Common Neuroses*, Edward Arnold & Co, 1937, p 131.
[1] Guthrie, Douglas, *A History of Medicine*, 1946, p 374.

Specialisation in Surgery

In surgery, specialities such as neurological surgery, orthopedics (bone and joint surgery), urology (bladder and kidney surgery) and thoracic surgery (heart and lung surgery), to mention a few, rapidly developed. In the present century a high degree of specialisation exists, and some people concerned with medical education wonder if those embarking on such a career should not have, from the beginning, a more extensive education in a narrower field. However, other thinkers feel that as greater understanding is reached in fundamental things, such as essential cell activity, genetic inheritance and the constitution of matter, certain medical, surgical and scientific disciplines, apparently now widely separated, will come closer together. In other words, when nature's deepest secrets are eventually understood, the final answers may lie in a few simple related truths rather than in a great diversity of complicated answers.[1] Those holding the latter view are not in favour of the introduction of changes which would further divide a complex and loosely knit profession.

[1] Todd, Sir Alexander, Introduction to *Chemistry in the Service of Medicine*, Pitman, London 1963.

Some important discoveries

Mendel and genetics

On a cold night in February 1865 an Augustinian monk by name Gregor Mendel (1822–84) read a paper to a small scientific society in Brunn, Austria. This paper contained the detailed results of certain experiments with garden peas which he had been carrying out for the past eight years. It must have been a great disappointment to him when no questions were asked and no discussion followed his paper. For thirty-five years his findings, printed in an obscure journal, remained completely unnoticed.

Medical history is full of examples of a prophet being without honour for a considerable time, but few, if any, discoveries of comparable magnitude have been so neglected during the lifetime of the discoverer. In 1900 through the independent efforts of three men, his work was rediscovered and recognised as marking an epoch in the study of life.

The principles of Mendel's laws in their simplest form can be demonstrated by the following experiments with two different varieties of 'four-o'clocks', one whose flowers are red and the other white. If pollen is taken from one flower and applied

to the pistils of the other, seeds will
eventually result. When planted these seeds
will produce plants with pink flowers.
These plants are known as hybrids. Seeds
from these hybrids will produce a further
series of plants which will have different-
coloured flowers—some red, some pink and
some white. These different colours always
occur in the ratio 1 : 2 : 1. The red and white
flowered plants of this generation always
breed true but the pink flowered plants
produce again three colours in the ratio
mentioned.

Modern research has shown that little
threads of protein which are contained in
the nuclei of the egg cell (ovum) and the
germ cell, and which are called
chromosomes, are the carriers of heredity.
The factors, carried in the chromosomes,
which are responsible for the development
of the various characteristics of the organism,
are called genes. If there occurs in a gene a
change which causes it to become a new
stable inheritable unit, it is said to have
undergone mutation. All the factors which
can cause such changes to occur are not yet
understood but some of them are known. For
example excess exposure to X-rays and other
forms of irradiation can cause gene changes.
For many reasons the study of genetics is of
the greatest medical importance. Because of
78

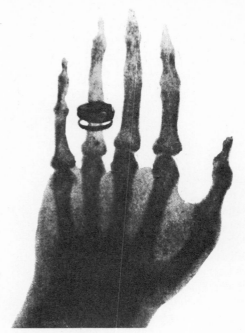

30 *'A new kind of ray'*

Mendel's discoveries, biology ceased to be a
speculative science, and doors to knowledge
still closed will eventually be opened.

The Discovery of X-rays
In November 1895 William Conrad
Roentgen (1845–1923) of Wurzburg,
Germany, was experimenting with what
were called cathode ray tubes. Using these,
two metal electrodes were sealed into a glass
tube and the air then sucked out by a vacuum
pump. If the electrodes were connected to a
suitable source of electric power, a golden-
green phosphorescence resulted. Roentgen
found, after a series of experiments, that
these activated tubes gave off an invisible
ray which could pass through some solid
substances and register on a photographic
plate.

31 *The dangerous effects of excessive X-ray exposure were not recognised at first*

32 *Professor and Mme Curie at work in their laboratory*

Thus were X-rays born. Originally they were used only in the diagnosis and treatment of fractures and some foreign bodies (e.g. a swallowed coin or a metallic splinter), but quite soon the scope of the procedure was extended. If the patient swallows or is injected with certain substances which are opaque to X-rays but not injurious to the body, various cavities and organs can be outlined and studied. Every year new developments in radiology take place and most of these are important. Few advances have relieved so much suffering and disability as have X-rays in the treatment of fractures, which is what their inventor

79

suggested seventy years ago. Unfortunately, it was not recognised at first that excessive doses of X-rays had the power to burn and permanently damage human tissues. Many an early practitioner met death or mutilation because of inadequate protection against constant exposure. Later the power of these rays to kill cells was harnessed and used in the treatment of malignant disease, the cells of which are usually more susceptible to the effects of X-rays than are normal tissue cells.

The Curies and Radium
Another notable discovery allied to X-rays was the discovery of radium by Pierre Curie (1859–1906) and his wife Marie (1867–1934). After removing one known substance after another from a ton of pitchblende they were eventually left with a fraction of a grain of a new element which they named radium. This gave medicine a powerful weapon that can be used in the treatment of some forms of cancer.

8 Medicine and surgery in the twentieth century

Many notable advances have occurred in medicine during this century. The story of most of these must await future historians who, as the years pass, will be better able to estimate the true significance of the new discoveries. It is difficult to put into some sort of order of importance such discoveries as vitamins, hormones, insulin, viruses, penicillin and other antibiotics, and a host of others. I have selected for discussion, from the hundreds of advances of this century, insulin and penicillin.

Diabetes and the discovery of insulin

Following the time of Claude Bernard, experimental investigations into the causation and treatment of diabetes had advanced but little. In 1869 attention was drawn to certain small islands of tissue in the pancreas gland. These were the so-called 'islets of Langerhans' named after the man who discovered them. The cells of these little areas differed very considerably in microscopic appearance from the normal pancreatic cells. It was noted that these islets had no ducts to drain off their particular secretions, and their resemblance to other ductless glands, such as the pituitary, thyroid and suprarenal glands, was observed. When it became known that in fatal cases of diabetes the 'islets of Langerhans' were wasted and destroyed, the stage was set for a great discovery. The man who made it was Sir Frederick Banting (1891–1941). He conceived the idea that if the duct of the pancreas of a living dog were tied and the digestive secretions prevented from escaping into the bowel, then perhaps the main part of the pancreas might shrivel up, leaving only the 'islets' which have no external ducts. Extracts of the remaining portions of the gland might contain the active principle of these small areas.

Banting did his work at the University of Toronto and his associate was Charles Best (born 1899). The extract which they prepared from the partly degenerated pancreas gland was called insulin, and it had the power when injected of reducing the level of sugar in the blood.

Since that time methods of production of insulin have become considerably simplified, and it is no longer necessary to tie off the pancreatic ducts of dogs and other animals.

The number of people suffering from diabetes varies in different countries and with different races. In Western countries about five people in every thousand suffer from the disease. At least half of these sufferers require insulin to enable them to live ; the importance of this discovery can hardly be overestimated.

Sir Alexander Fleming and the discovery of penicillin

One day in 1928, in a laboratory in St Mary's Hospital, London, a bacteriologist, Alexander Fleming (1881–1955), was examining a dish of culture media (see p 60) which had been inoculated with bacteria known as staphylococci. Fleming noticed that the culture had become contaminated with some mould from the air, which was not an uncommon occurrence. Something else had happened too, something that only the trained and discerning eye could see. Fleming saw that around the mould, the colonies of staphylococci had been dissolved, leaving what appeared to be minute drops of clear fluid. Eventually this mould, which was to become famous, was identified as a type of penicillium (penicillium notatum).

In 1929 Fleming read a paper to a scientific society and stated his discovery that a certain type of penicillium produces in culture a powerful antibacterial substance which does not either poison or irritate animal tissue even in large doses. He suggested that the substance might prove to be of value in the control and treatment of certain infections. At the time not much interest was shown.

It was not until 1939 that Doctors Florey and H. B. Chain started to work at Oxford on the difficult problems of concentrating penicillin in a stable and non-irritating form for clinical use. Eventually they were successful but the necessary processes were difficult and costly. At that time Britain had become involved in the life and death struggle of the last World War, and the nation's factories were in no condition to make the necessary effort. In 1941 Florey left for the United States, taking with him cultures of penicillium. Eventually the difficulties were overcome, and by 1943 penicillin was being produced in quantity and lives were being saved in their thousands.

Fleming was knighted in 1944, and in the following year, together with Doctors Florey[1] and Chain, was awarded the Nobel Prize for Medicine. When he died in 1955 he was buried in St Paul's. A lifelong friend and associate, Professor Pannet, delivered the funeral oration. In conclusion he said : 'His choice of a profession, his selection of a medical school, his deviation into bacteriology, the nature of the work he did,

[1] Now Lord Florey, President of the Royal Society of London.

82

the chance fall of a mould : all these events were surely not due to mere chance. We can almost see the finger of God pointed to the direction his career should take at every turn.'[1]

The Church and medicine in modern times

Ever since its earliest days, the Christian Church has traditionally cared for the sick, and its activities through certain nursing orders and missionary societies are well known. Perhaps not so well known is the work of certain dedicated individuals. Missionaries, medical or otherwise, seldom if ever have easy lives, and this is especially true at the present time. At home mention of the word missionary often produces slighting remarks about hymn-singers and Mother Hubbards ;[2] and abroad, accusations of espionage, imprisonment and death.[3]

No historian dealing fully with these missionary activities could overlook the magnificent work done by Father Damien

[1] Maurois, André, *The Life of Sir Alexander Fleming*, English version 1959, p 275.
[2] A rather unbecoming garment designed for native women in Victorian times ; it closely resembles the 'sack' models of the early 1960s.
[3] Carlson, Dr Paul, executed in the Congo, 1964.

(1840—89) among the lepers on the island of Molokai ; or the labours of Albert Schweitzer (1875—1965) who gave more than half a century of sacrificial work in a primitive hospital at Lambarene in French Equatorial Africa. His work was inspirational, essentially because he turned his back on the almost certain promise of intellectual fame and worldly success to follow an ideal. There are many such examples but only two will be mentioned in any detail, because their work was on a national scale.

Grenfell of Labrador

Wilfred Thomason Grenfell (1865—1940) studied medicine at the London Hospital where he came under the influence of Sir Frederick Treves. It would be fascinating to know what particular qualities the great teacher recognised in his pupil, but it is related that it was on Treves' advice that he formed in 1889 the Royal National Mission for Deep Sea Fishermen. For the next three years he worked in the North Sea area as a medical missionary. As a result of this experience he was chosen by the mission to develop a similar type of service to fishermen on the desolate Labrador coast of

Newfoundland. In the first two months of his work Grenfell attended more than 900 patients and he gradually won the respect and devotion not only of the fishing communities but also of the Eskimo tribes.

Gradually this immense work of relief spread along the Labrador coast, and public imagination was stimulated by his heroism and devotion.

In 1900 he was presented with the hospital ship *Strathconna* and he received support from friends in Canada, America and Britain. Grenfell was knighted in 1922 and retired in 1935. By this time the government had more than adequately met the needs of the communities on the Labrador coast, and Grenfell was able to lay down his burdens, secure in the knowledge that the work would go on.

'A mantle of safety': the Flying Doctor Service

The United States of America and Australia are approximately the same size, but there the similarity largely ends. The United States has about five times as much temperate land with a good rainfall and only about one-fifth as much arid country. The American frontiers were broached by waves of wagon trains, but the Australian outback was

84

infiltrated by ones and twos. Where the American settlers found the Mississippi and fertile prairies, their Australian counterparts found sandhills, salt-pans, eroded mountains and great heat.

In 1912 the white population of the Australian inland was less than 50,000[1]. The life of these pioneers was an extremely hard one. Home life was a rarity, there was no recreation and no way of getting news. Letters took weeks or months to arrive and loneliness lay like a dark cloud over an area the size of Western Europe. Perhaps the greatest dread was the danger of an accident or illness. A fall from a horse on the perimeter of a cattle station, 10,000 square miles in area, could quickly result in death, and no treatment was anywhere available for sickness.

The year 1912 is mentioned, for it was then that John Flynn (1880–1951), a thirty-one-year-old Presbyterian minister, decided to devote his life to the people of inland Australia. He realised that two essential problems had to be overcome: one was transportation and the other communication.

It took the 1914–18 War to point the way to the solution of the problems. War-time

[1] McPheat, Scott W., *John Flynn, Apostle to the Inland*, Hodder and Stoughton, 1963, pp 19–22.

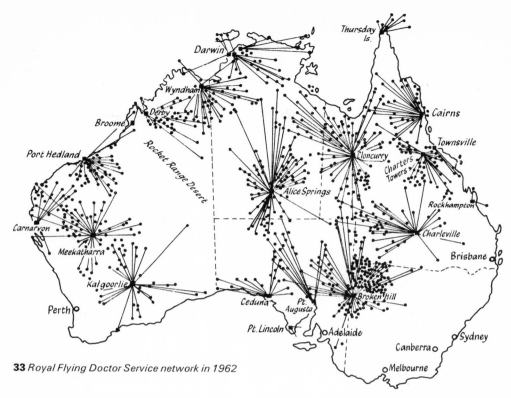

33 *Royal Flying Doctor Service network in 1962*

developments in aviation and radio were startling, and in 1917 John Flynn first voiced to a sceptical Australia his great idea. To have flying doctors working from inland bases, sweeping over deserts, mountains and floods with equal facility, surely was the answer. And how would these doctors be called? Well, would it not be possible to develop inexpensive transmitting and receiving radio sets which the ordinary man or woman could handle to call the doctor when he was needed?

Flynn's thinking was so far ahead of his time that naturally he encountered every sort of opposition. An approach to professional technicians to supply him with the necessary small radio sets was greeted with smiles of pity and headshaking. Such a thing had never been thought of and of course was quite impossible! Several years had to pass before Flynn's faith was justified. In 1928 the first medical flight was made from Cloncurry in Queensland, and in the following year, Alfred Traeger, an electrical engineer, solved the problem of radio communication. Power was supplied to the unit by using bicycle pedals, the hands being free for transmission and adjustments.

Thus the dream became a reality and the Flying Doctor Service of Australia grew and developed. At the present time it has thirteen bases which cover nine-tenths of the continent.

Near Tennants Creek, in Northern Australia, at the junction of the Stuart and Barkly highways, is a commemorative cairn

85

erected by the (now) Royal Flying Doctor
Service. Engraved on a plaque on this cairn
are these words :

COMMEMORATING

'FLYNN OF THE INLAND'

THE VERY REV. JOHN FLYNN, O.B.E., D.D.

OF THE PRESBYTERIAN CHURCH OF AUSTRALIA
1880–1951

His vision encompassed the continent.
He established the Australian Inland Mission
and founded the Flying Doctor Service.
He brought to lonely places a spiritual ministry
and spread a mantle of safety over them
by medicine, aviation and radio.

9 The future of medicine

Robert Louis Stevenson (1850—94), who was a consumptive, dedicated a volume of his poems (*Underwoods*) to the doctors who attended him, in these unforgettable words :

'There are men who stand above the common herd : the soldier, the sailor and the shepherd not infrequently ; the artist rarely ; rarelier still the clergyman ; the physician almost as a rule.

He is the flower (such as it is) of our civilisation . . . . He brings air and cheer into the sickroom, and often enough, though not as often as he wishes, brings healing.'

This is a magnificent tribute to a profession but will it be as deserved in the future as Stevenson thought it was when he wrote it ? To answer that it becomes necessary to make some sort of guess as to what medicine and doctors will be like in the future.

Excluding atomic tragedies, there seems little doubt that before the year 2000 the present world population of about three billion (a billion equals one thousand million) will be doubled ! Assuming that a two per cent population increase per year persists without alteration for 140 years, the world population will increase to fifty billion, a figure which is probably beyond the present capacity of the earth to carry. It would seem obvious that sooner or later some form of population limitation will be forced on the world. This problem, like that of the road toll, is something which most people deplore and then dismiss from their thoughts. However, it will eventually become everyone's problem, especially the doctors' of the future. With this population explosion, there is and will be a world-wide tendency for masses of people to move into cities in much the same way as they did during the Industrial Revolution.

This movement, which is becoming particularly evident in many of the developing countries, will obviously produce political, social and medical problems of the greatest complexity within the next twenty or thirty years. When numbers of country-people become city-dwellers, they bring rural ways to a city that is not prepared to receive them. Ways of coping with waste and refuse, which in a small village may not be particularly harmful, will, if introduced into the densely populated city, produce new hazards and dangers to health. Overcrowding, together with air pollution, noise, mosquito infestation, lack of water, of proper hygiene and sanitation, can easily combine to produce a situation which may become catastrophic.

Can anything be done about this ? Obviously sooner or later, and preferably sooner, something will have to be done to control this explosive increase in the world's population.

In Western countries the effect of modern medicine and the associated dramatic decline in the death-rate has not led to over-population because of an associated decline in the birth-rate, which apparently automatically occurs in societies which enjoy a high standard of living. Since the last World War, many of the advantages of modern medicine, hygiene and insect control have been applied in less highly developed nations. Because this has happened without any significant increase in general living standards, no reduction in the birth-rate has occurred.

Some experts believe that it would be possible to raise substantially the living standards in less developed countries if the more fortunately situated were prepared to give enough aid. This could be true and other than total war may well be the only solution. However the degree of sacrifice that would be demanded from the wealthier countries would be so great that it is unlikely that enough will be done until the obvious needs of self-preservation force the issue. Let us hope that it will not then be too late.[1]

What of the doctors themselves, who will be working in these changed conditions? Will they too have changed? Mention has been made previously of the complexities that are often involved in the making of a diagnosis. The idea of feeding data into a computor, which would analyse all the relevant information and quickly produce the correct answer, has great appeal to the planners of the future. In the opinion of some, within the next fifty years the application of scientifically based medicine to meet the needs of the sick person will be wholly the function of the hospitals, which will be staffed by experts and technicians, products of medicine's machine age, by then in its full flower.

However, there is a danger that this state of affairs may split the profession into two sections, those inside the walls and those outside. It has been suggested[2] that medical education should be modified so that those who have 'more interest in human beings than ideas' should be encouraged to concentrate on sciences concerned with human behaviour (psychology, psychiatry, etc.) rather than on laboratory ones. This is of course sound advice, but unfortunately there seems no proper place in this estimation of

[1] World Health Organisation, expert committee on environmental health aspects.

[2] Burnett, Sir F. M., *Medical Journal of Australia*, Vol 11, No 18, 1964, p 697.

the future for the individuals who from time to time reappear throughout the history of medicine — men with an intense love of their fellow men, and who also have ideas. Lister was one of such people and they are the *élite* of medicine.

For a long time it has been customary for medical planners, organisers, politicians and the like to refer to general practitioners as being 'the backbone of the profession'. This is rather an unfortunate phrase because in some countries there is an increasing tendency for general practitioners, by regulation and custom, to be deprived of status and backing so that eventually they become almost boneless.

In the medicine of the future the countries which have solved the problems of keeping their medical profession united, and not split into sections of varying status and importance, will probably in the long run have the best medical service. To quote the words of Walmsley (1964) :[1]

'We must remember that science resides in the intellect and not in instruments which lie installed within some hallowed sanctum.'

Einstein in 1931, lecturing to some students at an Institute of Technology in California, said :

[1] Walmsley, Robert, *Journal*, Royal College of Surgeons of Edinburgh, October 1964, p 3.

'It is not enough that you should understand about applied science, in order that your work may increase man's blessings. Concern for the man himself and his fate must always form the chief interest of all technical endeavours. Never forget that in the midst of your diagrams and equations.'

It is important for those of us who think about things to remember that this year is not the end of time. For many years to come there will be a steady world-wide progress towards health and leisure. Other material advances will be made and doctors will play a big part in bringing these things about. However, it is unlikely that much increase in happiness or even a fuller freedom will result, until man learns to seek perfection in himself as well as in his environment.

As the years go by, greater and greater will be the knowledge of the workings of man's mind and emotional life. As this knowledge increases, so will understanding, tolerance and happiness. When at last the darkest places are illuminated by the light of knowledge, then and then only will lasting progress occur, progress which will make our present-day achievements seem rather second rate.

This may seem a little difficult to believe, but there is no doubt that at present medicine is choked with facts and is daily becoming

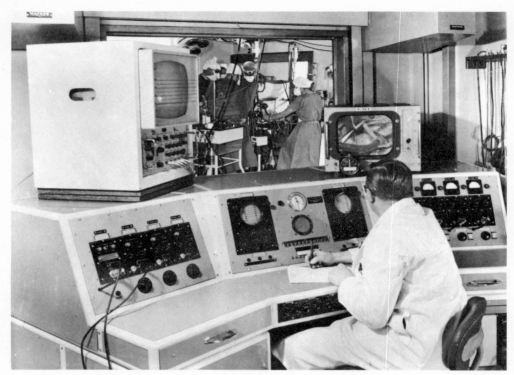

34 *An operation on the open heart at Hammersmith Hospital, London. The surgical team is seen in the background through the window. The electronic apparatus in the foreground is used for recording the body's vital functions during the course of the operation. The field of operation itself is seen on the television set above the technician's head*

more complicated. A science which is truly progressing tends to become simpler, not more difficult (see p 77). In medicine we await an intellect which can integrate the threads and patches of knowledge into a complete fabric, an all embracing but nevertheless understandable unity.

In the meantime, young doctors of today and the torch-bearers of the future, brothers in a great society, would do well never to forget the advice of a very wise man :[1]

'From inability to leave well alone.
From too much zeal for the new and
           contempt for the old.
From putting knowledge before wisdom and
      cleverness before common sense.
From treating patients as cases.
From making the cure of the disease more
     grievous than the endurance of the same.
O Lord deliver us.'

[1] Hutchison, Sir Robert (1871–1960), Edinburgh graduate, Physician to the London and Great Ormond Street Hospitals.

Therein lies the road to the stars.

A select booklist

by Norman Stone, A.L.A.

BANKOFF, GEORGE. *Milestones in Medicine*. Museum, 1961. Illus. A brief history from earliest times to the dawn of antibiotics.

CALDER, RITCHIE. *Medicine and Man: the story of the art and science of healing*. Allen & Unwin, 1958. Relates the practice of modern medicine to that of the ancients and folk culture.

DE KRUIF, PAUL. *Microbe Hunters*. Cape, reprinted 1963. The story of the men who helped in the battle against disease from the seventeenth to the twentieth century.

GUTHRIE, DOUGLAS. *A History of Medicine*. Nelson, 1945. Illus, booklist. For the more advanced student.

HAYWARD, JOHN. *The Romance of Medicine*. Routledge, 2nd edn 1945. Illus. A brief account of the history of medical science, the growth of the medical and nursing professions, and modern medicine and surgery.

IVES, A. G. L. *British Hospitals*. Collins (Britain in Pictures Series), 1948. Illus. An outline of British hospitals and their service to the public from the Middle Ages.

MARGERSON, DAVID. *Medicine as a Career*. Batsford, 1962. Illus. Contains appendices on medical schools of the United Kingdom and Eire.

STAROBINSKI, JEAN. *A History of Medicine*. Leisure Arts (The New Illustrated Library of Science and Invention Series), 1964. Illus, table. A brief history. Contains a useful chronological table.

THORWALD, J. *Science and Secrets of Early Medicine: Egypt, Mesopotamia, India, China, Mexico, Peru*. Thames & Hudson, 1962. Illus, booklist. For the advanced student.

TURNER, E. S. *Call the Doctor: a social history of medical men*. Joseph, 1958. Illus. A study of the doctor himself and of the varying esteem in which he has been held in the community.

VAUGHAN, PAUL. *Doctors' Commons: a short history of the British Medical Association*. Heinemann, 1959. Illus. For the advanced student.

Biography
CROWTHER, J. G. *Six Great Doctors*. Hamish Hamilton. Illus. Contains biographies of Harvey, Pasteur, Lister, Pavlov, Ross and Fleming.
SHIPPEN, K.B. *Men of Medicine*. Dobson. Illus.

WYMER, NORMAN. *Medical Scientists and Doctors*. Oxford. Illus. Contains biographies of Harvey, Pasteur, Lister, Anderson, Pavlov, Curie, Fleming and Schweitzer.

Individual Biography
Elizabeth Garrett Anderson
MANTON, JO. *Elizabeth Garrett Anderson*. Black.
Sir Frederick Banting
ROWLAND, JOHN. *The Insulin Man: the story of Sir Frederick Banting*. Lutterworth.
Elizabeth Blackwell
CHAMBERS, PEGGY. *A Doctor Alone: a biography of Elizabeth Blackwell, the first woman doctor, 1821–1910*. Bodley Head. Illus.
Marie Curie
CURIE, EVE. *Madame Curie*. Heinemann. Illus.
Sir Alexander Fleming
BULLOCK, W. A. C. *The Man who discovered Penicillin: a life of Sir Alexander Fleming*. Faber.

Wilfred Grenfell
STEVENSON, H. N. C. *Wilfred Grenfell.*
Black.

Edward Jenner
EBERLE, IRMENGARDE. *Edward Jenner and Smallpox Vaccination.* Chatto & Windus. Illus, table.

Joseph Lister
TRUAX,R. *Joseph Lister, father of modern surgery.* Harrap. Illus.

Louis Pasteur
DOORLY, E. *The Microbe Man: a life of Pasteur for children.* Heinemann. Illus.

Sir Ronald Ross
KAMM, JOSEPHINE. *Malaria Ross.* Methuen.

James Simpson
ROWLAND, JOHN. *The Chloroform Man: the story of James Simpson.* Lutterworth.

See also the booklist in the companion outline *The Story of Nursing*, by Jean McKinlay Calder.

Index

93